the Forth Naturalist and Historian

Volume 32 2009

Published by the Forth Naturalist and Historian, University of Stirling – charity SCO 13270.

ISSN 0309-7560

ISBN 978-1-898008-66-8

Supported by INEOS and Scottish Natural Heritage.

Cover: front– Spawning Arctic charr painting by Robin Ade (© Peter S.
　　　　Maitland)
　　　back– Corn marigolds on the Carse of Lecropt (photograph Roy
　　　　Sexton).

Printed by Meigle Colour Printers Ltd., Tweedbank Industrial Estate, Galashiels.
Set in Zapf Calligraphic on 115 gsm Satin and cover 300 gsm Satin.

THE FORTH NATURALIST AND HISTORIAN

The Forth Naturalist and Historian (FNH) is an informal enterprise of Stirling University. It was set up in 1975 by several University and Central Regional Council staff to provide a focus for interests, activities and publications of environmental, heritage and historical studies for the Forth area, comprising now local authority areas Stirling, Falkirk and Clackmannanshire.

Since then the organisation of an annual environment/heritage symposium called *Man and the Landscape* has been an important feature.

The annual *Forth Naturalist and Historian* has published numerous papers, many being authoritative and significant in their field, and includes annual reports of the weather, and of birds in the locality, plus book reviews and notes. These volumes provide a valuable successor to that basic resource *The Transactions of the Stirling Field and Archaeological Society*, 1878-1939. Four year contents/indexes are available, and selected papers are published in pamphlet form, while others are available as reprints.

In addition a 230 page book *Central Scotland – Land, Wildlife, People*, a natural history and heritage survey, was produced in 1994 and is available in the form of a CD-Rom, *Heart of Scotland's Environment* (HSE).

Other FNH and associated publications still in print include – *Mines and Minerals of the Ochils, Airthrey and Bridge of Allan, Woollen Mills of the Hillfoots, The Ochil Hills* – landscape, wildlife, heritage – an introduction with walks, *Alloa Tower and the Erskines of Mar*, and the *Lure of Loch Lomond* a journey round the shores and islands. Several of these are in association with Clackmannanshire Field Studies Society.

FNH publications are listed on the internet British Library (BLPC) and by booksellers e.g. Amazon, Bol, Barnes and Noble.

Offers of papers/notes for publication, and of presentations for symposia are ever welcome.

Honorary Secretary Marilyn Scott,
Computer Services, University of Stirling, FK9 4LA.
E-mail: fnh@stir.ac.uk
Web: http://www.fnh.stir.ac.uk

Author Addresses

Andrew Bain, 22 Clarendon Road, Linlithgow EH49 6AN

Neil Bielby, 56 Ochiltree, Dunblane FK15 0DF

David Flint, 30 Barn Lane, Oakley, Basingstoke RG23 7HT

Peter S. Maitland, Fish Conservation Centre, Gladshot, Haddington EH41 4NR

Ron Page, Kingarth, Airthrey Road, Stirling FK9 5PH

Michael F. Thomas, 16 Blairforkie Drive, Bridge of Allan FK9 4PH

CHANGES IN THE CONTROL OF EDUCATION IN STIRLINGSHIRE
1560–1930

Andrew Bain

It is sometimes assumed that secular control of local education in Scotland began only with the Education (Scotland) Act of 1872, and that links with the traditional, church system of the preceding three centuries were finally broken by the Education (Scotland) Act of 1918. In Stirlingshire at least this was not so, for here the process of change began in important ways before 1872, and continued in equally important ways beyond 1918. The history of that longer process – and in particular the contribution made by the final stage in Stirlingshire to Scottish education as a whole – is the theme of this article. To say this is not to deny the major contribution of these two Acts to a more modern system of Scottish education; it is merely to suggest that the process of change in Stirlingshire was longer than it is sometimes assumed to have been nationally.

One feature of the history of Scottish education that is generally accepted is the essential part that was played by the Churches of several denominations: in founding schools, in financial support, in shared control, in day-to-day administration, and in personal leadership at all levels.[1] Discussion will therefore consider the ways in which that part changed in Stirlingshire over time from a major to a much more marginal contribution. As only a single county, this geographically central shire was sometimes to a great extent representative of a wider, more national, transformation but in the final years of transition to more secular control it was of particular national interest as the traditional part played by the Churches responded to a more diversified kind of society with different aims, needs and priorities. In fact, events here in Stirlingshire affected the whole course of denominational schooling throughout Scotland. The conflict that arose in the 1920s between the Roman Catholic Church and the then Stirlingshire Education Authority led eventually to the House of Lords, whose judgement influenced the pattern of national provision thereafter. In order to convey the significance of that judgement – and to assess the importance of those final years as a whole – it will be necessary first of all to consider the wider context that was the traditional system of control of schools in Stirlingshire. This system developed over three centuries, a development that may be considered in four periods: before the Protestant Reformation; from the Reformation of 1560 to the Education Act of 1696; from 1696 until mid-eighteenth century; and from then until the Education Act of 1861.[2]

Very little is known with any confidence about the Catholic Church period that preceded the effects in Stirlingshire of the Protestant Reformation of 1560, and what is known suggests that schooling was attached either to formal religious institutions or to the Royal Burgh of Stirling itself.[3] The aspect of such provision that is central to this discussion is that control was thus in the hands of the Catholic Church or it was, by the middle of the sixteenth century, within the jurisdiction of members of the Town Council of Stirling, who now claimed the school as "their Grammar School" and administered it as such. Before the Reformation any formal schooling that was in existence at that time was closely controlled by a hierarchical church or by a relatively restricted Lay group whose school was for long the only burgh school in Stirlingshire.[4]

This type of control was to change at the Reformation, when the first national system of schools was planned upon the geographical basis of the church parish, a unit hitherto undervalued and underfinanced at a time when local resources had been used to support Catholic monastic institutions in the area. Post-Reformation Stirlingshire had 24 parishes, and it was upon the framework of these that the system was so planned as to have one church and one school in each, in order that the church and school would act together to ensure that congregations might be able to read the Bible for themselves rather than be dependent upon the Catholic priesthood as a mediator between God and man.

The national Acts of Parliament that were passed throughout the following 100 years incorporated and endeavoured to facilitate the plans of the Reformers, although these became truly effective only after the Act of 1696, which introduced the sanctions necessary for implementation of the pattern that had been set out in the preceding century.[5] In this second period, from 1560 until 1696, the heritors (landowners of a certain standing in the parish) were made responsible for providing a school, built or rented; for appointing a schoolmaster; and for supporting him with a legal salary. But in the vision of the times, this was a shared responsibility, with the tiered administration of the Reformed Church providing direct local oversight at presbyterial and parish level. In this way in Stirlingshire, the Presbyteries of Stirling, Linlithgow and Dumbarton – all conscientious bodies of ministers – were corporately responsible for examining the faith, morals and academic standards of masters chosen by the heritors, and for investigating any subsequent complaints about lapses in their faith, loyalty, behaviour and teaching. Additionally, each parish minister was, as an individual, held responsible for the day-to-day running of the school in his parish, which could additionally be examined at regular intervals by a district committee of ministers appointed by the local presbytery.

Unfortunately, the heritors in several places fell short of the ideal set them (sometimes from lack of personal concern; sometimes from sheer economic pressures) so that in practice the clergy of the Reformed Church became the dominant partner at this time. So, too, the nature of the physical environment and the distances involved made the provision of one legal school in each parish very often inadequate: for example in a large, physically rugged parish like Buchanan in western Stirlingshire. Thus, in instances of mismatch of any kind, be it of terrain or of population spread, it was often the local kirk session that was forced to take the initiative in supplying much-needed assistance in schooling.[6]

Thus, during this second period, the Reformed Church was at the very least a legislated partner in the control of local schools, and often the initiator of provision or improvement where either was required by local circumstances. All this was in accordance with the desire to introduce adequate elementary instruction for children who were to be taught to read as an aid to their religious salvation – and if possible also to write and count.

Such provision was, however, only the first tier of the reformers plan. This new kind society that they envisaged required leaders who were to be educated as well as instructed, and it was into this second tier that the ancient Grammar School of Stirling fitted. To this School future ministers, doctors and lawyers were to go, and so it became an essential part of the post-Reformation system, being at this time the only true grammar school in Stirlingshire, since that in Falkirk evolved from its parish school only much later.

The structure that had first been planned by the sixteenth century reformers and was later reinforced by legislation during the following century, became increasingly effective in Stirlingshire during the decades after the Act of 1696. This third period might have seen successful implementation of that structure of control but for the economic changes in the eighteenth century that transformed a predominantly rural society into one which became to a great extent industrial, commercial, and more heavily populated. To begin with, the traditional pattern continued for a time – the earliest secessions providing no other system of schools – but the national events of 1843 that led to the formation of the Free Church meant that large numbers of the population in Stirlingshire adopted alternative loyalties. From then on, there were in the County two well-developed educational systems, although it is interesting that, while the two denominations differed on some fundamental questions, their structures of local control for schools remained very similar, with no radical departure by the Free Church from the practical framework that had characterised the oversight of the Reformed Church.[7]

This process of major change in local loyalties through the provision of alternatives in church membership was accelerated by the social effects of the industrial and commercial diversification that was transforming central Scotland. Taken together, such changes in the structure of local society eroded the traditional sanctions of a single Church, and undermined during this fourth period its previously tight control of many patterns of community life – including its schools.

The most erosive of the secular changes taking place in the County were industrialisation and urbanisation. The expansion of the light castings industry in Falkirk and District from mid-nineteenth century onwards led to a complex of industry and commerce serviced by new roads, railways and canals. For example, communities like Bannockburn, Camelon, Kilsyth, and St. Ninians became nail-making centres, and those in Alva, Campsie, Denny, Muiravonside and Slamannan developed around the search for local supplies of essential coal, iron, and limestone. Population was consequently increased and redistributed, so that the needs of school provision became different from what they had been in a more rural County. Parish schools and churches had largely been settled near to each other, but both now often found themselves at a distance from the locations best able to serve their expanding indigenous and incoming population as it was regrouped and redistributed.[8] The educational plan of the reformers had been designed on the basis of relatively static communities; from now on in Stirlingshire the traditional Church had to begin to respond to changes in society rather than to oversee its own initiatives.

Around the middle of the nineteenth century, diversity had replaced any uniformity of educational provision in Stirlingshire. At that time there were to be found: the traditional parish schools, additional heritors schools, denominational schools, endowed schools, charity schools, subscription schools, infant schools, private schools, works schools, adventure schools, and of course the Grammar School of Stirling (later the High School). While the State began to play an increasing part by supporting some of these by grants, this support was as yet limited, extending in the 1860s to only 46 of the 165 schools in Stirlingshire.[9]

By 1861 Parliament was forced to acknowledge that piecemeal financial support was insufficient to cope with fundamental social change: radical structural alterations were required if it was to ensure efficiency; to get value for its increasing investment; to meet the demands of other denominations for an end to hierarchical control by a single Church; and to take into account the views of those who wished to have a system of schools that was both national and secular. The Act of 1861 was its first attempt to change in a fundamental way an inherited structure of control that was seen to be no longer working.[10]

It was really from this point – not from the Act of 1872 – that major separation began from the traditional type of control that had been exercised by the Presbyteries of Stirling, Linlithgow, and Dumbarton, and their kirk sessions. What the Act of 1861 did was to alter radically the balance of supervision between the heritors and the Church of Scotland. The Acts of 1803 and 1838 had at first confirmed and then marginally increased the relative powers of the heritors, but it was the Act of 1861 that radically altered the balance as the Church lost much of its right to oversee schools.[11] Some will see it as one of life's little ironies that following the Act of 1872 it was the heritors, as heritors, whose numbers and influence increasingly dwindled away, whereas it was the clergy who were able to retain a measure of influence by being able and willing to take advantage of the changing educational scene. They adapted to the new situation by contributing quite legally as individuals or in groups, after legislation had removed their previous rights to share corporately in a major way in local oversight. The local powers of the Church of Scotland were at a stroke curtailed by the Education Act of 1861. The local powers of the heritors, on the other hand, withered away in proportion as their membership of the School Boards introduced by the later Education Act of 1872 steadily declined, following their failure either to seek election at all or to be elected by the ratepayers.

Following experience, the findings of the Argyll Commission of the 1860s, and the increasing interest in wider representation in public affairs, both national and local, the Act of 1872 introduced a new balance in educational provision and control. Its purpose was to retain an element of local representation in decisions arising from the needs and wishes of local communities, within an increasingly tightly organised central control that would be achieved by means of Government grants; by the regulatory powers of a centralised body; by the oversight of visiting Government inspectors, and by an increasingly coherent system of training teachers.[12] That balance was to be achieved by the direct election every three years to the Local School Boards of those representatives who were judged most likely by the ratepayers to be able to secure their wishes and to meet their perceived needs. Stirlingshire was allocated 26 Boards originally, largely based upon the traditional parishes but allowing both Burgh and Parish (or Landward) Boards in areas of mixed density in the local population. In the County the most common membership of the Boards was five, seven, or nine, with a few being increased later to 11, but no centre of population was dense enough to require the maximum of 15 that was available nationally.

The national system of Cumulative Voting gave electors freedom to distribute as they wished as many votes as there were candidates, and was intended to be a means of ensuring that minority groups or individuals who would not previously have had a chance of being directly represented could be so. In Stirlingshire this freedom led to a wide social and occupational spread in success at the polls. Despite complaints and reservations in local newspapers about distortion of the general will, there seems little doubt that in the County, and in the country, this method of voting went a long way towards its purpose, and that, although not perfect, it was as fair a method as the times could provide. Its significance here was that, after three centuries of control by one social class and one Church, there was now in place a system that, over 46 years of its existence, saw Board members elected from more than 50 different occupations. The oversight of schools in Stirlingshire was no longer conducted by the unaccountable, who might, or might not, attend regular, or irregular, meetings; instead they were supervised by a nationally specified number of directly accountable representatives for a three-year period. For the first time, representatives of minorities were elected: Catholics, workers, and women all took their places along with representatives of the various Protestant Churches and of local industrial, commercial and mercantile interests. Concerns about education declared in election campaigns, the open election of candidates, and ever-vigilant local newspapers ensured a high percentage of individual attendance at all meetings.[13]

Those who complained that the use of the Cumulative Vote gave minority groups the power to frustrate what were alleged to be majority interests through their efficient organisation of support tended to overlook the fact that this was exactly the kind of democratic freedom that the new system of voting was designed to achieve. The philosopher John Stuart Mill's conviction that this was a system that would ensure fair representation of local communities and their local interests was confirmed by the findings of the nationally appointed Select Committee about its practice.[14] Nevertheless, it was not perfect, and the Single Transferrable Vote was introduced by the Act of 1918 in an attempt to make it more so. In this system, voters ranked their chosen candidates in order of preference, again having the right to vote for as many candidates as they wished, and having surplus votes transferred to the next ranked nominee on their list.

During those 46 years of the Boards from 1873 until 1919, the clergy who became members were elected from a number of denominations, the Church of Scotland parish minister having now no privileged place by virtue of his calling, but taking the same chance of election as any other nominee.

In total, the clergy remained throughout this period a relatively numerous and identifiable group, whose influence was increased by their often being chairmen at a time when no professional officers were appointed to undertake the heavy routine administration of a Board's affairs. Thus, although clerical influence had changed in its composition and in its means of expression as policy, in accordance with the changes made nationally in administrative procedures over the years, that influence at a certain level was still a significant one in Stirlingshire in the provision and maintenance of its schools.

The following is a detailed example from Stirling and Falkirk of the Burgh and Parish (Landward) Boards, showing as approximate percentages those who came from a landed background and those who were clergy.[15]

Table 1 Distribution (%) of clerics and land owners on School Boards

Election Year	18 73	76	79	82	85	88	91	94	97	19 00	03	06	09	11	14
Landed SB				11	11	11									
FB	28	28	28												
Clergy SB	22	11	11	33	44	44	33	22	22	22	22	22	111	11	9
FB	28	28	28	28	43	43	28	22	44	22	22	56	44	44	27
Landed SP *				20	40	20									
FP	43	43	43	43	57	28	14	14					14		
Clergy SP *															
FP	28	28	43	14	14	14	14	14	14	28	14	28	28	28	14

(SB = Stirling Burgh FB = Falkirk Burgh SP = Stirling Parish FP = Falkirk Parish)
* Stirling Parish Board amalgamated with Stirling Burgh Board in 1891

In the ten years that followed the Act of 1918, when the School Boards were replaced by a single ad hoc Education Authority for Stirlingshire, the influence of the clergy actually increased. Not only did their numbers form a considerable proportion of the Authority, but a disproportionate number were chairmen of influential sub-committees.[16]

Table 2 Clergy Membership of Education Authority Committees in 1919

Committee	Total Number of Members	Total Number of Clergy Members	Clergy Chairman
General	13	7	Yes
Finance	13	3	No
Bursary	13	7	Yes
Medical Inspection	13	5	No
Property	13	5	Yes
Staffing	13	9	No
Bible and Temperance	13	10	Yes
Chairman's	12	6	Yes

Thus, points of view and decision-making could sometimes represent clerical, or even denominational interests, and it is arguable that the course of one major development in the history of Scottish education was the direct result of clerical membership of the Authority. There would seem to be little doubt that the conflict of 1925-29 in Bonnybridge, which ended with the judgement of the House of Lords regarding the future of its Catholic school, and which affected schooling throughout Scotland, arose from the composition of the Stirlingshire Education Authority, an Authority largely dominated in numbers and influence by clergy of a traditional cast of mind. From this judgement that the Stirlingshire Education Authority was bound to accept the transfer of a Catholic School built after the Act of 1918, any such school could become the responsibility of an Education Authority, even although it was devoted to Catholic education given by Catholic teachers. Had the Stirlingshire Authority not been constituted as it was in the 1920s, Scottish education would not have been affected when it was in the way it was. Catholic schooling might well have developed, but it might not have taken the Scottish courts and a final judgement of the House of Lords to determine its timing and its nature. Other denominational minorities having previously accepted the provisions made for them within the public system, it was the Catholics who were able to take full, and future, advantage on a national scale of this Stirlingshire ruling.[17]

Notwithstanding the timing of the Bonnybridge Case (as it came to be called), the years of the School Boards in Stirlingshire from 1873 until 1919 and the ten years of the Stirlingshire Education Authority that followed may be considered as a single period that expressed the same fundamental view of the place of local participation within an increasingly centralised national system of schooling. The underlying principle of democratic, open, and directly accountable representation for a limited period after which the electors had another opportunity to assess stewardship was the same from 1873 until 1929:

only the best way of achieving it was altered in 1919. In the perspective of the 300 years of control in Stirlingshire that went before, and the years of control by Stirlingshire County Council that followed, with education as only one of its many functions, this period of 56 years was characterised by directly accountable representation of local educational interests. The Act of 1918, which addressed itself to perceived weaknesses that arose nationally from differences of geographical size, of district finance, of numbers of members, and of diversity of aims and policies among the School Boards, changed many aspects of education, but did not alter the fundamental principle of direct local participation in the oversight of local schools.

It was the Local Government Act of 1929 that introduced a recognisably more modem structure of administration of schools. In Stirlingshire, the ad hoc Education Authority was replaced by an Education Committee of Stirlingshire County Council, a Council responsible for many aspects of local government. The election procedure for the Council itself was democratic, but its Education Committee was subsequently chosen by the parent body, and from 1930 onwards direct clerical influence declined as the proportion of clergy decreased in a larger Education Committee than the Authority had been. Thus, the local contribution of the Churches, however it may have outlasted the participation of the heritors, did eventually shrink also to proportions that were more in keeping with changing times. This contraction of clerical membership comes out clearly in a comparison of percentages before and after the Act. [18]

Table 3 Contraction of Clerical Membership of Education Authority Committees 1928-31

	1928	1931
	%	%
Full Authority/Full Committee	41	14
Bible, Temperance, Rural Library	53	26
Bursary	47	5
Chairman's	40	33
Medical, Attendance, Contin. Classes	33	15
Property	13	10
Staffing	60	20

Whether Stirlingshire was entirely representative of the history of education in Scotland during these centuries of development from the shared local control between heritors and parish ministers of the Church of Scotland right through to a more modern system of oversight, only a detailed study of many localities will show. [19] Certainly in this one county the participation and influence of the local clergy demonstrably survived for a longer period than is sometimes thought, and it was only in the 1930s that they moved from the centre to the periphery in their influence upon the further development of the County's educational system. The usual landmarks may therefore to some extent be misleading.

Sources and References

The following list is brief, and in the main refers to the local research undertaken in Stirlingshire upon which the article is based. Many other relevant sources are given in James Craigie's two volumes and the Jordanhill computerised lists of records.

1. The most accessible general histories of the period are:
   Robert D. Anderson: *Education and the Scottish People, 1750-1918* (1995).
   Lindsay Paterson: *Scottish Education in the Twentieth Century* (2003).
   James Scotland: *The History of Scottish Education,* Vols.1 and 2 (1969).

   The discussion of Stirlingshire's own history of education is largely based upon the detailed research reported in:
   Andrew Bain: *The History of Education in Stirlingshire from the Reformation to the Act of 1872* (1965).
   Three into One (2003) – Grangemouth School Board.
   Ancient and Modern (2006) – Stirling and Falkirk Boards.
   Changing Patterns in the Local Control of Education (2008) – Stirlingshire.

2. A detailed account of these earlier periods may be found in Bain: *The History of Education In Stirlingshire* (1965).

3. The history of the Grammar School (later High School) is contained in detail in A.F. Hutchison: *The High School of Stirling* (1904).

4. Falkirk had a Burgh School from the nineteenth century, but this evolved from the earlier Parish School and a short period as the Grammar and Parish School (See James Love: Schools and Schoolmasters of Falkirk (1898).

5. The Education Acts in full were printed, and a complete list is given in the two volumes of James Craigie's *A Bibliography of Scottish Education* (1970, 1974). Relevant sections are readily available in Anderson and Scotland (See above). See also H.M. Knox: *250 Years of Scottish Education,* 1696-1946 (1953).

6. *The History of Education in Stirlingshire,* Ch. III (see Bain above).

7. Contemporary assessments are to be found in the Reports of the Education Commission (Scotland), 1865-68

8. For details of the local changes that took place during the nineteenth century, see: *The History of Education in Stirlingshire,* Ch.VIII. (see Bain above).

9. *Second Report of the Education (Scotland) Commission* (1867), pp.39-41.

10. See, e.g, Bain: *From Church to State,* Introduction (1993).

11. Anderson (1995); Scotland (1969). For the way in which teachers were particularly affected, see Scotland, Vol 1, pp.229 onwards.

12. For a general discussion of the period of the Local School Boards, see Anderson (1995); Paterson (2003); Scotland, Vol. 2 (1969).

13. *The Stirling Observer* and *The Falkirk Herald* both contain readily accessible and detailed reports of all elections. (Stirling Council Archives and Falkirk Council Archives).

14. John Stuart Mill's view of the Cumulative Vote is given on page 39 of M. Atkinson's *Local Government in Scotland* (1904). An assessment of the Cumulative Vote in practice appeared in the *Parliarnentary Papers* for 1884-85, xxx, pp.295, 673, 718.

15. A full comparison with the occupations of other members is given in Bain: *Ancient and Modern* (2006), pp.77,78.

16. Records of the Stirlingshire Education Authority, 1919-1930. Detailed reports are also given in *The Stirling Observer* and *The Falkirk Herald*.

17. The full context and the detailed judgements of Lord Murray, Lord Ormidale and The House of Lords are preserved as copies in Falkirk Council Archives as A 1050. A number of newspapers and journals reported and commented: e.g. *The Stirling Observer*, *The Times*, and the *Journal of the Educational Institute of Scotland*.

18. Records of the Stirlingshire Education Authority, 1919-1930. Records of the Education Committee of Stirling County Council.

19. As long ago as 1951, Dr. John Mason suggested that no authoritative general history of Scottish education could be written until a detailed survey had first been made of each county's own peculiar history and problems. Much history of Scottish education has been written since then, but generalisations can still be arrived at in the absence of that knowledge: for example, against a background of rightful concern about the part played by women in local education, their significant contribution in some areas of Scotland can be overlooked.

JANET REID (1777-1854)
FORGOTTEN POETESS OF CARNOCK AND BRIDGE OF ALLAN
People of the Forth (17)

David A. Flint

Against me, some people has a clamour,
For in my little poems, there is no grammar —
Such reek as in the house must come out at the lum —
My little unpolished poems does please some.
Many a one cries out to me for fun,
But such things as Burns did write, by me shall ne'er be done.

From *On Edinburgh City* by Janet Reid

My quest for Janet Reid began at the closing-down sale in April 1999 of D.M. Beach's, a second-hand bookshop in Salisbury. Under a pile of books on the bottom shelf of the poetry section I discovered an album titled *Rhymes by Janet Reid, Carnock*. It had a leather spine, marbled boards, matching marbled endpapers, and the top edges of the leaves were coated in gilt. The armorial book plate of Peter Forbes was on the front endpaper. Inside were 35 broadsides all with a decorative border of printer's flowers, each tipped onto a single leaf. The broadsides were poems in rhyming couplets with an irregular metre and some mentioned dates in the 1840s. The "poetess" named herself at the foot of the poems as "Janet Reid, Carnock" or "Janet Reid, Carnock, Fifeshire" or "Janet Reid, Bridge of Allan". The broadsides had evidently been collected in the 1840s and acquired later by Peter Forbes who put them into this purpose-made album probably in the 1880s. Intrigued, I set off to Scotland in pursuit of Janet Reid!

In 1850 Major John Alexander Henderson (1806-1858) commissioned the 25-year-old Rev Charles Roger (1825-1890) of Dunfermline to write a guide to the Scottish watering place he was developing on the Westerton Estate at the village of Bridge of Allan. The guide was published in 1851 as *A Week at Bridge of Allan Comprising an Account of the Spa and a Series of Six Excursions around the Rising Watering-place*[1] and in it Charles Roger describes Janet Reid:

Of the present characters of the place the most conspicuous is the poetess, Janet Reid, one of the best specimens of the class to which she belongs. Janet writes or utters poetry, such as it is, on any subject, with complete facility, on a moment's warning, and being devoid of anything satirical in her nature, universally indulges in eulogistic strains. Her published pieces are numerous, and by the vending of these to visitors, on their way to and from the Well House, she not only has contrived to eke out a livelihood, but to realize a considerable competency to meet the wants of declining days. Most poets, in whatever state they may have begun life, generally die poor;

Janet promises to prove an exception; she may probably leave the world, through the good-natured liberality of the visitors at Bridge of Allan, comparatively rich.

Janet Reid must have protested to Charles Roger at this supposition because in the 2nd edition of *A Week at Bridge of Allan* published in 1852 he repeats the first two sentences but then curtails his comments on her earnings to:

Her printed pieces are numerous and by the vending of these to the visitors at the Well House she has contrived to eke out a decent livelihood.

This amended description is given again in the 3rd edition published in 1853. A facsimile reprint of this edition was published by Jamieson Munroe for Stirling District Libraries in 1996.

In 1853 Charles Roger came to Bridge of Allan as a minister of the Church of Scotland and established a "preaching station". In 1855 he was appointed chaplain to the garrison at Stirling Castle. *A Week at Bridge of Allan* was published annually with the amended description until 1858 but in the 9th edition published in 1859 Charles Rogers (he called himself Rogers from 1855) writes:

In the former editions of this work we noticed two persons, Janet Reid and singing Johnnie, as the characters of the place. These have both been removed from the scene without leaving any successors. Some of Janet's doggerel verses are still circulated for the amusement of visitors.

J. Malcolm Allan archivist of the Dr W.H. Welsh Educational and Historical Trust at Bridge of Allan searched the Stirling County archives for the two entries on Janet Reid listed in *The Stirling Observer Index: People 1836-1856*[2]. The first is a tongue-in-cheek poem about Janet Reid printed in *The Stirling Observer* on 25 June 1846:

Janet Reid
The Bridge of Allan Poetess

A' ye by braes of Bridge of Allan,
What's this that now has ye befallen?
I rede ye a', baith man an callan',
     To tak' gude heed —
Ane kent in Highland glen an' lawlan
     Is Janet Reid.

Douce Janet weilds a pithy pen,
A ten-horse power o' critic men,
There's nought o' ill within her ken
     But shaws' the deed —
She hurls back mischief to its den —
     Bauld Janet Reid.

Wi' Landon's taste, and Heman's power,
Or Dante's dark Satanic lower,
She mak's even infancy to cower
        Wi' shrinkin' dread —
Keen satire fa's in heavy shower
        Frae Janet Reid.

Nae coaches now on Sundays run —
That triumph honest Janet won —
The coaching trade is a' but done,
        Tween this and Tweed,
Nane shoots wi' sic a killin' gun
        As Janet Reid.

Philp leaves the new hotel, tis said,
And Barr has ta'en his weary bed —
Nae horse to stable now is led
        To get his feed —
And e'en the tollman now is fled:
        Thanks! Janet Reid.

Nae droskies now drive to Blawlowan,
To crush the lily or the gowan —
Gig wheels nae mair our streets are ploughin'
        At railway speed —
The grass on ilka highway's growin'
        Bless! Janet Reid.

Her verse is o' that kindlin' kind,
That speaks alike to heart and mind —
The chiel, indeed, maun een be blind,
        Past a' remead,
Wha sees nae satire, wit, combin'd
        In Janet Reid.

Tis true, she's no ower nice wi' rhyme —
A harmless fault, but no a crime —
The step "ridic'lous" and "sublime"
        Is worthless creed —
Nane tak's the forelock grip o' time
        Like Janet Reid.

The bonnie lasses braw an' fair,
Wha visit here for change o' air,
In whirling phaetons flee nae mair
        By glen or mead —
"Shank's naigie now, they just maun share"
        Quo' Janet Reid.

Blawlowan 1846 R.G.

Robert Philp and Matthew Barr were the respective keepers of the Royal Hotel and the Airthrey Well Hotel (later The Queens Hotel) at Bridge of Allan. Janet Reid must have composed a poem about the Toll at the east end of the Old Brig over the Allan Water but it has not been found. "Shank's naigie now, they just maun share" is probably quoted from another of Janet Reid's poems about Sabbath-keeping that remains undiscovered. Blawlowan is the only building left of the old village of Pathfoot on the outskirts of Bridge of Allan on the minor road towards Sheriff Muir. It was once an inn but in the 1840s it was owned by James Bryce who provided lodgings for visitors according to *The Tourist's Companion through Stirling* edited by John Forbes (1848) [3].

"R.G." had probably come to take the mineral waters at the Airthrey Well House. J. Malcolm Allan suggests that he was probably Robert Gilfillan (1798-1850) a minor poet who composed in Scots. He was born at Dunfermline but spent most of his life in Leith and in 1831 he published his *Original Songs* of ballads and love songs. One of his poems *The Maid of Allan* is included in *A Week at Bridge of Allan*.

Carnock, the home put on Janet Reid's earliest broadsides, is 5 miles west of Dunfermline. The 11 broadsides of poems by Janet Reid kept on the reserved shelves of the Local History Collection in Dunfermline Carnegie Library were given by Erskine Beveridge (1853-1920). In *A Bibliography of Works Relating to Dunfermline and the West of Fife* privately printed in 1901 he lists 18 broadsides by Janet Reid [4]. These were the 11 broadsides in his possession plus 6 additional titles out of the 11 listed at that time in the short-title catalogue of the British Museum (they are now in the British Library) plus another "on outside authority" titled *On Peace in Every Church* which has not been found. He then adds "and many more" and remarks of Janet Reid:

> *Born at Saline, 1777; resident at Carnock 1825-1840 or later; quite a character in her way – that of composing doggerel rhymes upon any (or every) subject. These she had printed in broadside form, commencing about 1836 and sold them from door to door. Latterly she removed to Bridge of Allan where she died. It is said that Jenny [sic] Reid was unable to write but her neighbours did this for her.*

Two anonymous notes, both written in the same hand, are kept with Janet Reid's broadsides in Dunfermline Carnegie Library. These notes were evidently sent with the broadside of *On the Honourable Manufacturers of Dunfermline* when it was given to Erskine Beveridge as a token of goodwill because it mentions "Mr Beveridge". This "Mr Beveridge" was his father also named Erskine Beveridge (1803-1864) who began work as a draper in the High Street at Dunfermline in 1823 and then started weaving damask linen in 1833 and later became the largest employer in the town.

The first note dated 31 July 1894 sent to Erskine Beveridge junior is a greeting. The second note (sent at the same time as the first note and written on a folded leaf of paper which held the broadside) is almost certainly a rough-and-ready but misunderstood version of the story dated 19 September 1840 written in pen and ink by a different hand on the back of the broadside of *On the Mid-Mill* in Peter Forbes' album:

> *Janet Reid is 63. First beginning of her poetry was about four years since when some of her neighbours were wishing to give a coat to the Bellman – a young man had written the Subscription paper & after she had got subscriptions the young man took away the paper again & the old man did not get his coat – Janet was angry at this & made a copy of verses on him – & recited it to the neighbours in revenge – they approved of it & urged her to do more & once Captain Wemyss who the Carnock folk wanted to be made a Parliament man and on whom she had made a long poem sent her a pound. This encouraged her to go on altho' she thought shame of it at first – she cannot write but her neighbours write her verses for her. Was born in Salon near Carnock in the West Neuk of Fyfe – has lived in Carnock 15 years.*
>
> *19 Sept 1840*

Janet Reid must have told this story to the buyer of the broadside that day. The Bellman was the parish crier. "Salon" is the village of Saline which is 2 miles north of Carnock – so Janet Reid moved from Saline to Carnock in 1825. Peter Forbes probably wrote both the notes sent with the broadside to Erskine Beveridge. There are marks in his album indicating the removal of a broadside.

The births and marriages before 1900 of the Reids in Fife are listed in the *International Genealogical Index*. These show that Janet Reid was the daughter of John Reid and Janet Malcolm; and that Janet had a younger sister named Helen. Extracts from the Old Parochial Registers were obtained which are now available through the website *Scotlandspeople*. They record the marriage of Janet's parents on 27 December 1776; the birth of Janet on 9 November 1777 and her baptism on 16 November 1777; and the baptism of her younger sister Helen on 18 March 1781, all at Saline. John Reid and Janet Malcolm are both described as living in the parish of Saline and he is described as a "weaver in Sandydub", then the name of a farm lying about a mile outside Saline on the minor road going to Dollar. This farm is now named Shieldbank.

The second entry on Janet Reid found in *The Stirling Observer Index: People 1836-1856* [2] is her obituary which was printed in *The Stirling Observer* on the 31 August 1854. The obituary is unsigned but it was probably written by Charles Roger judging by its wordiness: "a man of words … millions of words" writes J. Malcolm Allan in *The Forth Naturalist and Historian* Volume 13 (1990) [5] and by the last sentence of the obituary which is almost apologetic:

The Bridge of Allan Poetess

Janet Reid, the poetess of Bridge of Allan, is no more. She had long been in an ailing state, yet she wore well, and, a few weeks ago, died of old age. We know but little of her history before she came to this district, some 12 or 15 years ago. She belonged to the parish of Carnock, in Fife, and it was a benevolent feeling which first prompted her to attempt stringing verses together. The beadle of the parish had done something to excite Janet's sympathies, and as he was a poor man, and had to go some distance (no doubt sometimes in coarse and indifferent weather) to ring the bell, she thought it would be well if he had a great-coat to keep his old body comfortable, and she resolved to raise one for him by subscription. In this, however, she failed, but resolving not to be foiled in her endeavours, she betook herself to publication, and generously devoted the proceeds to this humane object, and the bellman's coat was at length purchased in Stirling, and sent to him. Janet knew mankind too well to commit the efforts of her genius to the mere publishing community; with laudable industry, after her effusions had been committed to paper by some fair amanuensis, for as she said herself –

"The pen, that valuable thing, I ne'er was learnt to use,"

she had them printed, in the first instance, on single slips, with a border round them, and then, with her stock in trade, set off through the country disposing of them upon easy terms, at one penny each, though some good-natured persons would give her 6d and a "comfortable cup of tea" to the bargain. In this simple but efficient mode of publication, Janet continued for a number of years, when the ambitious idea struck her of having selections from her "works", which had now become numerous, separately published in the gorgeous style of a sixpenny volume. We know not what number, if any, of this "Adition" of her works remain; but she never again had recourse to the same mode of publication, though she still continued to write, or rather to dictate, up to a period within a little of her death. Janet's style of composition is beyond all criticism. The iambics, dactyles, spondees and other prosodial lumber, with which all our inferior poets from Milton downwards have used to help themselves and their readers, were totally disregarded by Janet, as unworthy of her notice. With her the notion of compressing the idea within the line never had a place. The line must be extended to hold the idea, however numerous its feet might be. Sometimes a broad octavo page would not contain a line, while again a fourth of the space was quite sufficient. The great cause of Janet's popularity consisted in a good-natured easy and *gash* garrulity, quite free from scandal, while tinged with a religious and benevolent feeling, which sat easily upon her, and which never assumed an air of bigotry or sham. She was a calm, steady, and, generally speaking, a cheerful body, and her end was in keeping with the even tenour of her way. She was well seen to at last, and enjoyed as much kindly attention as her circumstances admitted. Her closing days, thanks to a few considerate ladies, were surrounded with every comfort she could enjoy; an attentive nurse was provided her; and she passed away in peace. Janet's poetry was exempt from criticism, but she produced something better than good poetry, namely, an inoffensive life. The little money she had saved passed into the hands of her relatives.

The particular quotation in her obituary comes from her poem *On Edinburgh City*. Janet Reid says in her poem *On Giving Work to Working Folk* that she "never could use" a pen. In her poem *On Children Going to Church* she says that she "never was at school" and in her poem *On Edinburgh City* she adds that she dictated her poems:

> *For my uneven lines you will excuse,*
> *For the pen, that valuable thing, I was never learned to use.*
> *Thanks to the youths that my poems did write,*
> *Although I sat by them and to them did dite.*

But in her poem *On the Jolly Tailors* she recalls that:

> *When I was young, a boy of me did take great care,*
> *And learned me to read when he had time to spare.*

At that time, as required by law, there was a school in every parish in Scotland but there were not places for every child to attend and each subject had its price. So a child could learn to read at school but not to write and sometimes girls were not sent to school at all. Janet Reid was evidently not sent to school and probably earned her living as an agricultural worker from childhood. In her poem *On the Farmers* she says:

> *For the Farmers I hae always had great respect —*
> *For my welfare in former years they did not neglect.*

In 1837 when she was 60 and no longer able to work in the fields Janet Reid used her ability to compose poems to earn a living. The alternative was reliance on the parochial poor fund. She had her poems printed and sold them by going door-to-door around Carnock, Saline, the neighbouring villages, and Dunfermline. In her poem *On the Mid-Mill* she says:

> *I'm not now able the harvest for to shear;*
> *I thank the public for many a penny and half-penny to me they do spare.*

In 1840 Janet Reid, taking a big step, left her home at Carnock. Her subsequent journeys can be deduced from the subjects of her poems, from the dates of their composition, from the dates of the printings of her broadsides, and from the towns where they were printed. An act was passed in 1799 that required printers to put their names and addresses on their work; but this was not always done. She set out on her travels in 1840 after composing *On the Mid-Mill* (a mill, now a private house, which stands 4 miles from Carnock) in which she says "Ere ever the year 'Forty comes round again" and before composing *On Glasgow, Bonny Town* which ends "My Glasgow friends, this was written in the year Eighteen-Forty for you".

This is how Janet Reid seems to have journeyed though she might have made more moves and she might have visited other towns; she probably visited Paisley whenever she went to Glasgow; and she would have gone between Saline, Carnock and Dunfermline or between Bridge of Allan, Dunblane and Stirling whenever she wanted:

1777-1825: Saline
1825-1837: Carnock
1837-1840: Carnock – Saline – Dunfermline – Torryburn – Carnock
1840: Carnock – Dunfermline – Edinburgh – Glasgow – Paisley – Falkirk (?)
1841: Falkirk (?) – Stirling – Torryburn – Carnock – Bridge of Allan –
        Dunblane – Glasgow
1842: Glasgow – Paisley – Stirling – Bridge of Allan – Glasgow
1843: Glasgow – Paisley – Edinburgh – Stirling – Bridge of Allan – Edinburgh
1844: Edinburgh – Glasgow – Paisley – Stirling – Bridge of Allan
1845: Bridge of Allan
1846: Bridge of Allan – Carnock – Bridge of Allan
1847-1854: Bridge of Allan

It is not possible to identify Janet Reid with certainty in the census held on the night of Sunday 6 June 1841 but she was probably the Janet Reid staying at Torryburn in Fife 2 miles from Carnock. She had probably returned to sell her broadsides at the Carnock Fair held annually on the 26th May and she might have been staying with friends.

The census held on the night of Sunday 30 March 1851 in the parish of Logie records Janet Reid living on the "High Road (the Turnpike Road)", now Henderson Street at Bridge of Allan. She was lodging with James Kepson an agricultural labourer, his wife Margaret and their two children. Janet Reid is shown as unmarried, aged 73, having the occupation "poetess", and as born at Saline in Fife. The 1841 and 1851 censuses for Logie also record a Thomas Reid born in 1808 at Saline in Fife. In 1851 he was a fishmonger living at 18 Rose Street in Bridge of Allan with his wife Janet and their two sons. Perhaps they were relatives of Janet Reid.

Janet Reid at first appears to have put her home on her broadsides as Carnock, then as Carnock, Fifeshire from late in 1842, and then as Bridge of Allan from towards the end of 1843. She finally settled at Bridge of Allan in 1844 probably when the Airthrey Well House opened for the whole year rather than for the season from April to September. That she first visited Bridge of Allan in 1841 is shown by her poem *On the Bonny Alley Tree* printed in 1846. It seems likely that Janet composed it when she was about to return back to Fife and visit the Carnock Fair held on 26 May 1846 – and perhaps, in the words of Charles Roger, "comparatively rich":

> *For five long years have I been dwallin'*
> *At the bonny Brig o' Allan.*
> *Now I am returning back in wealth,*
> *And, thank God for't, in good health.*

Newspapers in the early 1800s were dull – and expensive too until stamp duty was abolished in 1855. Broadsides were the popular reading matter for over three hundred years. Their text might be verse, prose, song or a mixture of these. They could be religious, political, criminal, romantic, amatory, bawdy, humorous, superstitious, moralistic or tragic. Nearly all were composed anonymously. Broadsides were bought in bulk from the printers by hawkers who then sold them on the streets for a halfpenny or a penny each. At that time street-sellers cried their wares and Janet Reid probably "chaunted" (an archaic word) her verses on the streets. Leslie Shepard explains in *The History of Street Literature* 1973 why so few broadsides have survived [6]:

> *In the nineteenth century there was a final tremendous outpouring of every kind of street literature, just before the introduction of cheap books and newspapers. Thousands upon thousands of broadsides and chap-books swept like a tidal wave over the streets and market-places. And as the tide receded much of this fragile ephemera disappeared leaving only the souvenirs secured by thoughtful collectors.*

Janet Reid's poems and broadsides can usually be dated to within a year. Sometimes she quotes a date or mentions an event that can be dated. A few broadsides have dates put on them as footnotes. Printers at that time were short of type so her poems were reset each time they were printed usually with varied punctuation; and each printer used different printer's flowers. From time to time she made changes to her poems or even changed the title. Each printing of a poem is therefore different. These differences help in determining their chronological order and in attributing dates to them.

She usually stuck with the printers that she had used before. In Edinburgh she used Macdonald in Carrubbers' Close, a family of printers according to the *Scottish Book Trade Index* [7]. In Glasgow she used Hugh Baird in Trongate at first, but from 1843 she used William Gilchrist who moved between several addresses. At Paisley she used the partners John Neilson and Thomas Graham who worked individually within the same workshop. When she was visiting or living at Bridge of Allan she always used the Stirling Observer Office. Six of the broadsides found have no printer's imprint but the printer of three of them can be deduced as Macdonald from the similarity of the printer's flowers and the type-faces. Two of the others, *On the Honourable Manufacturers of Dunfermline* and *On the Gallant Sailors*, may have been printed at Dunfermline and *On the Year 1841* may have been printed at Falkirk.

Janet Reid seems to have gone to her printers about once a month judging from the footnotes put on her broadsides by William Gilchrist in Glasgow who printed *On a Comfortable Cup of Tea* dated March 1842 and *On Glasgow's Bonny City* and *Against Sabbath Breakers* both dated April 1842. She probably had up to a dozen poems printed as broadsides in one batch which would be as many as she could reasonably carry around. Three clusters of nine, ten and eleven broadsides (each of these clusters almost certainly printed in the same batch having the same printer's flowers and the same type fount for the printer's imprint) suggest that three collectors bought one copy of each of the poems she had with her as souvenirs of Bridge of Allan in 1842, 1843 and 1846.

Some of her poems were reprinted for years and she identifies a few of them in subheadings as "editions" - probably the number of times they were printed. Broadsides of the 15th edition of *On Children Going to Church*, of the 7th and 8th editions of *On Glasgow's Bonny City*, of the 11th, 13th and 17th editions of *On Humility* and of the 24th, 26th and 32nd editions of *On a Comfortable Cup of Tea* have been found. Charles Roger makes a pun of this in her obituary by referring to the "adition" to her works published in "the gorgeous style of a sixpenny volume".

A copy of this little chapbook is held in Glasgow University Library. It is titled *Poems on Various Subjects* by Janet Reid of Bridge of Allan and it was privately printed in the Stirling Observer Office in 1846. It has 36 pages and includes 34 of her poems 13 of which have not been found as broadsides.

Sixty different poems by Janet Reid have been discovered – 47 as broadsides and 13 only in her chapbook. How many poems did she compose in all? She probably began composing in 1837 and she continued composing into 1853, a period of 16 years. It is evident that in 1842 she had her poems printed at the rate of about one new poem a month. Even allowing for a lower rate in her early and later years she must have composed well over one hundred poems. Only two of the poems composed after 1846 have been found. It appears that copies of only about half her poems have been found.

Seventy-one broadsides of Janet Reid's poems have been found including duplicate copies of three of them. The 71 comprise a single broadside of 33 poems, two broadsides of 8 poems, three broadsides of *On the Gallant Sailors*, *The Queen's Farewell*, and *On Glasgow, Bonny Town* or *On Glasgow's Bonny City* (the same poem with a change in title), four broadsides of *On Humility* and *On the Spring*, and five broadsides of *On a Comfortable Cup of Tea*. The number of 'survivors' is probably another indication of the popularity of the individual poems.

How many broadsides did Janet Reid have printed during those 16 years? She would have had to earn at least the average income of a male agricultural worker. In *The New Statistical Account of Scotland* (1834-45) the Rev William Robertson at Logie near Bridge of Allan gives this as 10s (shillings) a week which was 20d (old pence) a day [8]. This would have been nearly double what she used to earn as a female agricultural worker, but even so she would have had to live frugally. So to pay for her lodgings, her transport and her printer she would have had to sell at least 50 broadsides a day for six days a week at a halfpenny or a penny each ... or 240,000 copies over the 16 years.

Most likely she had to buy a minimum print run of a gross (144 copies). Leslie Shepard in *The History of Street Literature* quotes a price of one shilling (12 old pence) a gross as the trade price for a quarter-sheet broadside [6]. So Janet Reid had to pay the printer 12 old pence a poem or up to 144 old pence in total each month. Her earnings probably fluctuated seasonally throughout the year

– but she had to keep selling her broadsides all year round, in all weathers, until she died in 1854.

There is no gravestone for Janet Reid in Logie Old Kirkyard, nor in Logie churchyard opened in 1809, nor in Lecropt churchyard (all near Bridge of Allan), nor in Saline Old Kirkyard, nor in the old burial ground in Carnock churchyard. In *The New Statistical Account of Scotland* (1834-45) the Rev William Robertson minister at Logie the parish in which Janet Reid lived writes: "There has been no register of deaths or burials kept in this parish except in the years 1761 and 1763" [8]. There is no record of her burial in the lair books or burial records in the County Archives of Stirlingshire nor of Fife; and the lair book for Saline 1811-1854 appears not to have survived. There is no inscription for her in *East Stirlingshire Monumental Inscriptions Pre-1855* [9] nor in *Fifeshire Monumental Inscriptions (Pre-1855): The Western Parishes* [10]. Perhaps her relatives took her back to Saline, 15 miles from Bridge of Allan, to be buried but probably Janet Reid was buried in Logie churchyard. Her poems are her memorial.

Janet Reid hawked her unpolished poems around the towns in the Central Belt of Scotland over 40 years before William McGonagall sold his poetic gems on the streets of Dundee. Janet Reid's poems are not amusing – not even unintentionally – and she overdid her religious exhortations. Understandably many of her poems, such as the eulogies on the towns she visited and in praise of different trades, were composed with an eye to sales. But in *On Cruel Murder* she tells how she helped to free a mother wrongly accused of killing a child at Carnock; she gave the profit made from selling *On an Accident at the Brig o' Allan* to the injured workman's family; she urges the rich to help the poor in *On the Distress of the Working Classes*; and she speaks out against cruelty to horses in *Be Merciful to Body and to Beast*.

A trilogy of poems composed by Janet Reid entitled *For Young Ladies*, *For Gentlemen and Ladies* (or *For Ladies and Gentlemen*) and *For Bachelors* are feminist. She trumpets their theme at the start of *For Young Ladies*: "Now, as Queen Victoria the throne has got / Young Ladies to choose their husband should have a vote". But the flavour of Janet Reid's verse is best savoured in the third of these poems:

For Bachelors

Bachelors, we all must understand,
Must surely be afraid to take a young Lady by the hand.
Bachelors must surely think much of their money,
That they are afraid to make a young Lady their honey.
If any man wishes to live comfortable through life,
He will take some pleasant young woman for his wife.
God said it was not good for man to be alone,
But that surely Bachelors never yet has known.
God said he would make for man a help that was meet,
But that help Bachelors never does seek.
I hope good people will understand,
That there is many a pleasant young Lady in the land.

A Bachelor for a young Lady might have a good seat,
And to take home a young Lady they need not be very far beat.
I have set the young Ladies now on a plan,
To try for themselves to get a young man.
A long time have Kings been on the throne,
But now that time for Bachelors has gone.
It will be a long time ere ever we will have a King again:
I hope good luck with the Ladies all that time will remain.
I hope Gentlemen and Ladies will live a religious life,
And married or unmarried, I hope they will never live in strife;
For in our country there is many a pleasant wife.
Married or unmarried we contented should be,
For many alterations we every year do see.
Time with every one is wearing away;
There will be neither marrying nor giving in marriage at the last day.
People's minds are ready to be full of vanity,
But neither rich nor poor can death defy.
Both young and old, rich and poor,
Must some day or night come to a dying hour.

Most of the 1800 broadsides reproduced on the website of the National Library of Scotland under *The Word on the Street* [11] are of plain text or are embellished with a crude woodcut picture. Only 30 have a border of printer's flowers. Janet must have asked her printers to use the printer's flowers which give a touch of elegance to her broadsides. Perhaps she was inspired by religious tracts on which printer's flowers were more often used. She was a remarkable woman who overcame her lack of education. Although she never married, it is evident from her poems that she would have liked to have had a husband. She fended for herself and must have been dogged, determined and hardy. She was outspoken in her views and her unpolished poems can be read with sociological interest – and pleasure.

Probably another fifty or more of Janet Reid's poems, most of them composed between 1847 and 1854, have not been found. I hope to republish her poems before long and I would welcome details of any further discoveries.

Her Works

The attribution for each of Janet Reid's poems is the year of composition of the poem which is the year of its first printing. The poems are put in order of the attributed year. They are also put into a possible chronological order within each year. The attribution for each of her broadsides or each poem in her chapbook is the year of its printing.

An unqualified "year" indicates that a date is given in the poem or an event is given that can be dated. A qualified "[year]" put within square brackets indicates that no date is given or no event is given that can be dated or if one is given it is evidently a later printing but a date can be attributed from other evidence. A qualified "[year?]" with a question mark put within square brackets

Milsey Bank Female School.

This School was visited by four ministers that day,
And much good of the teacher the gentlemen had to say.
The worthy gentleman in Keir presents did them send ;
He wishes them much of their youth in religion to spend.
He has long been a worthy gentleman about this place ;
He wishes both old and young daily to grow in grace.
I think each of them on their presents should put his name,
Or else they surely will be to blame,
That the children may have his worthy name to read
After he is numbered among the dead.
The ministers gave the children all a good advice,
To learn in their young years for to be wise.
They told them both evening and morning for to pray—
For time with them, both old and young, is flying fast away.
They all agreed that the teacher was leading them wisely on,
And the children to these gentlemen did sing a heavenly song.
I hope they will often see what is within their Bible,
And in searching the Scriptures they will not be idle.
The children of Israel's wanderings there they will see—
And away from every idol I hope they will flee.
Be sure to fly from the dangers of the Church of Rome,
For that by every one should be done.
There is too much evil in our nation ;
But by the Church of Rome we need not be brought into vexation.
But their worthy teacher will them direct ;
And the young ones for her will always have respect.
I think it a very good thing to teach them in a school by their lone,
That the big ones would not abuse them on their road going home.
The little children have always good will to go to school ;
Their teacher will teach them on the road never to act the fool.
I hope she and her scholars will hereafter each other see,
Where sun nor moon will never need to be.

JANET REID, Bridge of Allan.

Janet Reid composed *Milsey Bank Female School* probably in 1844 which was when the new Free Church school for older children was opened in Bridge of Allan. Milsey Bank House was originally built as a Bank for the mills on the Allan Water. "The worthy gentleman in Keir" was Archibald Stirling (1769-1847) laird of Keir. Milsey Bank House still stands above the west bank of the Allan Water at Bridge of Allan.

indicates that no date is given or no event is given that can be dated or if one is given it is evidently a later printing but a year is assumed which is probably right though there is insufficient evidence to warrant a certain attribution.

An unqualified but suffixed "year #" indicates that the broadside is one of a batch almost certainly printed at the same time of which the year of printing of at least one of the broadsides is known and can be attributed to the others.

Key to the Sources

(D) **Dunfermline Carnegie Library**:
> 11 broadsides collected by Erskine Beveridge listed in *A Bibliography of Works Relating to Dunfermline and the West of Fife* (1901) [4].

(NLS) The **National Library of Scotland**, Edinburgh:
> (a) 1 broadside acquired post 1975.
> (b) 1 broadside in an album *Street Literature* is among the 1,800 broadsides put online by the NLS under *The Word on the Street* [11].

(M) The **Mitchell Library**, Glasgow:
> 9 broadsides bound together as *Some of the Works of Janet Reid, the Bridge of Allan Poetess, Native of Carnock, Fifeshire*.

(BL) The **British Library**, London:
> (a) 11 broadsides bound together acquired by the British Museum before 1901.
> (b) 2 broadsides in an album *Poetical Scrap Book* collected by the Rev Francis John Stainforth.

(W) The **Wellcome Library for the History and Understanding of Medicine**, London:
> 1 broadside appended by accident to a medical leaflet (1836).

(PF) **Peter Forbes' album**:
> 35 broadsides in an album *Rhymes by Janet Reid, Carnock* collected by Peter Forbes.

(G) **Glasgow University Library**:
> 34 poems in a chapbook *Poems on Various Subjects* by Janet Reid collected by David Murray.

The titles of the poems are suffixed by the "(date)" given in the poem put within curved brackets; or by the "[date]" of an event mentioned in the poem that can be dated put within square brackets; and by the sources of the poem indicated by the Key letters plus the edition (where applicable) and the attributed dates of the printings.

Year / title / date in poem / source and year of printing   Attribution

1837

On the Honourable Manufacturers of Dunfermline [1837]: D [1839?]   1837
On the Spring: PF [1840], PF [1842], M [1842], PF 1843#, G 1846   [1837?]

1838

Lament for a Beloved Minister [1838]: PF [1840]   1838
On a Comfortable Cup of Tea: NLSb [1840?], PF [1840?], M 24th ed. 1842,
    D 26th ed. 1842#, BLa 32nd ed. 1846#, G 1846   [1838?]
On Children Going to Church: PF 15th ed. 1843#, G 1846   [1838?]
On the Gallant Sailors [1838]: PF [1838?], M [1842], D 1842#, G 1846   [1838]

1839

On the Gallant Shoemakers (1839): PF [1840], M [1842]   1839
On Humility: PF and M 11th ed. [1842] (duplicates), D 13th ed. 1842#,
    BLa 17th ed. 1846#, G 1846   [1839?]
On Giving Work to Working Folk: PF 1840   [1839?]
On Cruel Murder: W [1840?]   [1839?]

1840

On the Mid-Mill (1840): PF 1840   1840
On an Unfortunate Lady [1840]: PF [1844]   1840
On Glasgow, Bonny Town (1840): PF 1840 or *On Glasgow's Bonny City*
    (a change in title): PF 7th ed. 1842,
        D 8th ed. 1842#   1840
On Pretty Paisley (1 September) [1840]: PF [1842?]   1840

1841

On the Year 1841 (1 January 1841): NLSa 1841   1841
On Dunblane: M 1842   [1841]
In Speaking be Mild: PF [1842]   [1841?]

1842

On the Year Forty-Two (1 January 1842): G 1842   1842
Against Sabbath Breakers [21 February 1842]: PF and M 1842 (duplicates)   1842
Melancholy Accident (21 March 1842): PF and M 1842 (duplicates)   1842
On Airthrey Water: PF 1843#, G 1846   [1842]
On Airthrey Well House [1842]: PF 1843#   1842
On The Bonny Brig o' Allan [1842]: PF [1843], BLb [1850?], G 1846   1842
For Young Ladies: D 1842#, PF 1843#   [1842]
For Gentlemen and Ladies: PF 1843# or *For Ladies and Gentlemen*
    (a change in title): BLa 1846#, G 1846   [1842]
For Bachelors: D 1842#, BLa 1846#, G 1846   [1842]
On an Accident at the Brig o' Allan (18 June 1842): D 1842   1842
On Vanity Fair (6 August 1842): D 1842, G 1846   1842
On Drapers and Grocers [29 August 1842]: PF [1843]   1842
A Check for Scoffers [1 September1842]: D 1842, PF [1843], G 1846   1842
The Queen's Farewell (13 September 1842): D 1842, PF 1843#, BLa 1846#,
    G 1846   1842

1843

For the New Year (1 January 1843): PF 1843   1843
On the Faithful Ministers of the Church of Scotland [January 1843]: PF [1843] 1843
On Respectable Bakers: PF [1843]   [1843]
On Edinburgh City [21 February 1842]: PF [1843], BLa 1846#, G 1846   [1843]

On Peace in Every Church (recorded but not found) [18 May 1843]   [1843]
Be Merciful to Body and to Beast: PF 1843#, G 1846   [1843]
On the Loss of the Pegasus Steamer (20 July 1843): PF 1843, G 1846   1843
On Van Amburgh's Exhibition at Bridge of Allan (8 September 1843): M 1843 1843

1844

On the Year 1844 (1 January 1844): PF 1844   1844
On the Distress of the Working Classes: PF [1844], G 1842   [1844]
On the Reading-Room [1844]: G 1846   1844
On the Bonny New Church at the Bridge of Allan (1843) [1844]: G 1846   1844
On the Opening of the New School at Bridge of Allan (4 November 1844):
    G 1846   1844
Milsey Bank Female School [1844]: PF [1844]   [1844]

1845

On the Farmers: G 1846   [1845]
On the Gardeners: G 1846   [1845]
On the Shoemakers: G 1846   [1845]
On the Jolly Tailors: G 1846   [1845]
On the Fleshers: G 1846   [1845]
Against Sabbath Breaking: BLa 1846#, G 1846   [1845]
On a Day of Humiliation: G 1846   [1845]
On the Seventh of November (7 November 1845): BLa 1846# or
    On the Loss of the Potatoes (a change in title):
    G 1846   1845

1846

On the Bonny Alley Tree (1838 in retrospect) [1846]: G 1846   1846
On the Rev. Mr Brand's Death, in Dunfermline (1838 in retrospect): G 1846 [1846]
On a Pleasant Young Gentleman [1846]: G 1846   1846
On Glasgow's Bonny City (a new poem): BLa 1846#, G 1846   [1846]
On Barr's Bonny Hotel (1846): BLa 1846, G 1846   1846
On Philp's Bonny Royal Hotel [1846]: BLa 1846#, G 1846   1846
Poems on Various Subjects (a chapbook of 34 poems 1846): G 1846   1846

1850

On a Jack-daw, on the Banks of the Allan: BLb [1850?]   [1850?]

1853

On the Year 1853 (1 January 1853): M 1853   1853

References

1. *A Week at Bridge of Allan Comprising an Account of the Spa and a Series of Six Excursions around the Rising Watering Place* (subtitle varies with the edition), Charles Roger, Edinburgh: W.N. Lizars 1851; Edinburgh: Adam and Charles Black, 2nd ed. 1853 and 9th ed. 1859; and 3rd ed. 1853 Jamieson Munroe facsimile 1996.
2. *The Stirling Observer Index, People 1836-1856*, Stirling District Libraries 1988.
3. *The Tourist's Companion through Stirling*, ed. John Forbes, Stirling, 2nd ed. 1848.
4. *A Bibliography of Works Relating to Dunfermline and the West of Fife*, Erskine Beveridge, Dunfermline: William Clark and Son 1901.

5. *People of the Forth: Who Was Charles Rogers?* J. Malcolm Allan *The Forth Naturalist and Historian*, Vol. 13, 1990, pp 97-107.

6. *The History of Street Literature: The Story of Broadside Ballads, Chapbooks, Proclamations, News-Sheets, Election Bills, Tracts, Pamphlets, Cocks, Catchpennies, and other Ephemera*, Leslie Shepard, David and Charles 1973.

7. *Scottish Book Trade Index*, an online resource of the National Library of Scotland.

8. *The New Statistical Account of Scotland by the Ministers of the Respective Parishes* (1834-45), Edinburgh: W. Blackwood 1845.

9. *East Stirlingshire Monumental Inscriptions Pre-1855*, John Fowler Mitchell and Sheila Mitchell, *The Scottish Genealogy Society*, 1997.

10. *Fifeshire Monumental Inscriptions (Pre-1855), Vol. 2 The Western Parishes*, John Fowler Mitchell and Sheila Mitchell ed. Stuart E. Fleming, *The Scottish Genealogy Society* 2001.

11. *The Word on the Street*, an online resource of the National Library of Scotland.

PLANT RECORDS 2008-9

Plant Local Action Network is an informal grouping of botanists from the Forth catchments whose objective is to assist with the monitoring and conservation of the local flora. The group has been invited to write up some of the findings featured in its annual newsletter for the Forth Naturalist and Historian Journal.

Participants: Liz Alberts, Bob Cook, Ann Duncombe, Mary Gooch, Jan Harbidge, Jane Jones, Liz Lavery, John and Penny Lee, Sarah Longrigg, John Mitchell, Pam Murdoch, Sue Pringle, Eleanor Strain, Roy and Sue Sexton, John Snodin, Paul Stanley, Edna Stewart, Paul Taylor and Heather Young (Contact; Roy Sexton RoyGravedigger@aol.com)

The Flowers that Bloom in the Spring: A Comparison with 160 Year Old Records

It is widely assumed that global warming will bring forward the opening of spring flowers. This is not necessarily the case since, although the flowering of some plants is temperature-dependent, others use day-length as a trigger. Unfortunately we have not been able to find good local phenological records to use for comparative purposes. However, in 1849, Dr J.H. Balfour recorded the plants in flower around Bridge of Allan during the first week of April and later, after a mild winter, in 1881 Dr A. Croall made a similar list during the same week.

To investigate if these early timings had changed, members recorded the flowering of plants on a combined Balfour-Croall list during the first week of April 2008 and 2009. Defining what is meant by 'in flower' is a problem. While some plants like celandine were flowering in profusion others, such as cowslip, required a search of hundreds of plants before any were found that were in bloom. For future comparative purposes the populations were scored as: flowering over (o), frequently in flower (f), rarely in flower (r), not found in bloom (n). The survey was restricted to plants in the wild within approximately 5 miles of Stirling (Table 1).

Just as in the original lists, snowdrops were over and some coltsfoots were past their best but all the rest of the species could be found in bloom. One might have anticipated more in the 'flowering over' category if spring had advanced substantially but the converse was true with a significant proportion of species only just coming out. The general consensus was that there had been little change over the intervening 160 years and, if anything, flowering was a few days later. This conclusion is inconsistent with the averaged UK data of Sparks and Collinson (2003) which showed lesser celandine and blackthorn were blooming 17 and 27 days earlier than 13 years previously. Scottish data gathered by Scottish Natural Heritage were predominately too variable to show significant trends (Gaywood, 2006) but a wonderful set of records from a garden in East Lothian demonstrated that flowering of early native species had advanced approximately a day a year over the period 1978-2001 (Roberts *et al.*, 2004). A number of other common species blooming during our survey not mentioned on the Balfour-Croall lists included: barren strawberry (f), garlic mustard (f), germander speedwell (r), shining cranesbill (r), Spanish bluebell (r) and thale cress (f)

The wallflowers Dr Balfour saw at Dunblane Cathedral have long been banished from the stonework but they can still be seen round Stirling Castle walls. Unfortunately there is currently not enough to cover *'the weather beaten rocks of our castle with a mantle of gold'* (McDougall, 1882) their place having been taken by plantings of municipal daffodils. Sadly sweet violets (*Viola odorata*) are no longer *'found in great profusion in the woods behind Bridge of Allan'* having been replaced by the scentless dog violet (*Viola riviniana*). Bob Cook found a colony of the former by the ancient sycamore known as 'Granny's Staircase' on the old road between Menstrie and Alva (NS 8618 9728).

Butterburs (*Petasites hybridus*) are survivors and the colony outside the entrance to Stirling University seems to have thrived in spite of the footpath that has been constructed through it. John Mitchell pointed out that most butterbur plants are male, the much rarer females having a less compact inflorescence. A large colony of the latter can be found on the south verge of the A811 near Kippen (NS 6441 9542) (Figure 1). The giant butterbur (*Petasites japonicus*) is an introduced plant which, when in bud in February, resembles a

Table 1 Plants in flower within five miles of Stirling during the first week of April 2008 and 2009. Flowering over (o), frequently in flower (f), rarely in flower (r), not in flower (n). (Common names are taken from *Wild Flowers of Britain and Ireland* by Blamey Fitter and Fitter, 2003).

Common Name	Status	Common Name	Status
Blackthorn	f	Ivy-leaved speedwell	f
Broom	r	Lesser celandine	f
Butter-burr	f	Marsh marigold	f
Common woodrush	f	Opposite leaved golden saxifrage	f
Coltsfoot	f	Primrose	f
Cowslip	r	Purple dead nettle	r
Daisy	f	Red campion	r
Dandelion	f	Shepherd's purse	f
Dog violet	f	Snowdrop	o
Dog's mercury	f	Sweet cicely	r
Elm	f	Sweet violet	f
Field horsetail	f	Wallflower	r
Forget-me-not	r	White dead nettle	r
Gooseberry	f	Whitlow grass	f
Gorse	f	Wild strawberry	f
Ground ivy	r	Willows	f
Groundsel	f	Wood anemone	f
Hairy bittercress	f	Wood sorrel	r
Hazel	f		

small cauliflower. It has spread from gardens near Cromlix (NN 7881 0556) down the river Allan to Sandy Pines in Bridge of Allan (NS 7875 98961). Only 100 m behind it is a fellow traveller: the spectacular American skunk-cabbage (*Lysichiton americanus*) with its evil smell and massive yellow spadix. This plant is becoming common in several local rivers.

Both the authors of these early records deserve comment. John Hutton Balfour was Professor of Botany at Glasgow and Edinburgh Universities as well as Keeper of the Royal Botanic Gardens in Edinburgh. He became famous when he was accused of trespassing while leading a botanical excursion on the Duke of Atholl's land in 1847. The notorious 'Battle o' Glen Tilt' ensued between Balfour's students and the Duke's retainers. The ensuing law suit eventually resulted in Scotland's liberal countryside access rights (Gilmour, 1944). Alexander Croall was the first curator of the Stirling Smith Art Gallery and Museum (1874-85). He wrote a beautifully illustrated four volume guide to *British Seaweeds* which is much sought after by collectors. The illustrations were produced by 'nature printing' – a process involving placing the seaweed between a steel plate and a lead plate and then passing the sandwich between two heavy rollers. The high pressures generated imbedded the seaweed into the lead leaving a very detailed impression. Several coloured inks were then applied to the stamped plate, a copy being produced from one pull of the press.

Mistletoe, Toothwort and Bird's-Nest Orchids.

Toothwort (*Lathraea squamaria*) is a very peculiar looking ghost like plant with no green colour and scales instead of leaves. The pale pink flowering shoots are said to look like half a denture, the lilac-pink flowers resembling discoloured molars projecting from one side of a curving, fleshy, jaw-like stalk. It is a complete parasite obtaining all the water, minerals and nutrients necessary for its growth from its host. This it achieves by developing haustoria or connections between its roots and those of another plant. It has been traditionally found in Dollar Glen but although we failed to find it there seventy to a hundred flowering spikes appeared down-stream parasitic upon a large willow in a private garden where the Dollar Burn meets the river Devon (NS 9652 9700). Another smaller colony was later found even farther down on the north bank footpath approximately 600 m below the B913 bridge (NS 9541 9727).

During a search for rusty back fern in Blairlogie a resident drew our attention to the mistletoe growing on apple trees in the orchard on the east side of the village (NS 8273 9684). This is a hemiparasite since although the green leaves are capable of photosynthesis it is essentially rooted into the branches of its host from which it obtains minerals and water. Mistletoe is rare in Scotland and, according to the *Atlas of the British Flora,* is currently only recorded at one other site. Mistletoe seeds are spread by birds such as the mistle thrush. The bird grips the berry in its bill, squeezes the sticky coated seed out to the side, and then wipes its bill clean on a suitable branch. The seeds are coated with a sticky material called viscin, which hardens and attaches the seed firmly to its future host. In this case however the apple trees are thought to have been infected artificially.

In 2008 30 flowering spikes of the bird's-nest orchid (*Neottia nidus-avis*) were recorded between Bridge of Allan and Dunblane in Kippenrait Glen (NS7956 9963). Most of the orchids could be seen from the old road under beech trees. This site was first reported by William Hutton Forrest in the list of plants, published in 1831, which were considered to be of interest to visitors to Airthrey Mineral Springs. 2008 marked its spread into the adjacent beech woodland besides the Cock's Burn at Drumdruills (NS7919 9893). The bird's-nest orchid has no leaves or chlorophyll and is a parasite which is dependent on a fungus for its nutrients. Like most orchids, the minute seeds will not germinate until they are infected with the appropriate fungus which enters the orchid cells. The bird's-nest orchid remains totally dependent on the fungus throughout its life extracting nutrients from the fungal hyphae unlike other orchids which become partially or totally independent as they develop chlorophyll and leaves. Using DNA sequencing the fungus within the *Neottia* tissues has been identified as *Sebacina–like*, a type of jelly fungus that produces a white fruiting body that incrusts the bases of living plants. This group of fungi produce mycorrhizal hyphal-root connections with beech and other trees raising the possibility that the fungus obtains its carbon compounds from the beech and then the orchid in turn extracts them from the fungus (McKendrick *et al*, 2002).

Notes from Vice County 86

VC 86 (or Stirling) includes the old Victorian County of Stirling which encompasses modern Falkirk. It covers the watershed to the south of the Forth from Milngavie in the west to Grangemouth in the east. The Botanical Society of the British Isles (BSBI) recorder for the area is Edna Stewart (Contact: edna.stewart@ntlworld.com).

The frog orchid (*Coeloglossum viride*) has recently been made a UK Biodiversity Action Plan *'priority species'* as a consequence of declining numbers. Searches of several recorded sites such as the Little Corrie of Balglass (NS 5744 8465) and Touch Hills (NS 7302 9170) have been unsuccessful, though it is a very inconspicuous plant and difficult to spot. Fortunately it is still present on Dumbrock Muir (NS 5494 7833) and unexpectedly in the forestry plantation on Balgair Muir (NS 6039 9074). Here up to 70 plants flower every year in an old cornstone quarry which was once in open grassland but is now surrounded by mature spruce. The same quarry contains *Berberis vulgaris* which is quite rare and field gentian (*Gentianella campestris*) which can be found along the sides of the forestry track.

The ex-mining village of Plean may seem an unlikely place to describe as an orchid Mecca, however huge numbers of the greater butterfly orchid (*Platanthera chlorantha*) can be found there. The glorious meadow in Plean Country Park next to the ruins of Plean House (NS 8311 8661) had 2500 flowering spikes in 2008 following an incredible 3855 in 2006 (counted by Falkirk Scottish Wildlife Trust). Sadly building permission was granted for the meadow directly behind East Plean Primary School which contained a further 1500 spikes. This example illustrates how impotent the Scottish Government biodiversity conservation guidelines are. In the last five years similar meadows have been lost to show-jumping and trail bike racing.

Two invasive non-native plants have established an unwelcome presence in the area. The American water fern *Azolla fillicoides* almost entirely covered Airthrey Loch with several centimetres of solid growth. To create clear water for ducks the vegetation had to be held back by a boom. There was a similar but less extensive invasion reported in 1992 (Lassiere, 1992). The pirri-pirri-bur (*Acaena novae-zealandiae)* has become a serious problem on Lindisfarne where notices warn tourists not to venture into the dunes because the very sticky burs rapidly cover clothing and dogs' fur. A similar species *Acaena ovalifolia* was noticed five years ago in Murrayshall Quarry at Cambusbarron (NS 7704 9140). Surveys in 2009 showed it had spread alarmingly into the surrounding woodlands on Gillies Hill. The plant is already becoming increasingly common on forestry tracks in the Loch Lomond and Trossachs National Park and the proposed reopening of the Murrayshall Quarry will exacerbate its spread.

In 1977 Crockart reported an unusually prolific flowering of the rare yellow star of Bethlehem (*Gagea lutea*) in the woods on the northwest side of Kings Park (NS 7797 9335), the sight reminding him of Wordsworth's daffodils. This beautiful little bulbous plant has long been known in the woodland near the Home Steads at the base of the slope below the golf course (McDougall, 1882) and was collected from the site for exhibition at the Glasgow Natural History Society meeting in 1887. Aided by compass bearings taken by Bob Cook in 1977, many of those who saw it in the past have searched in vain to relocate the colony. It seems that the levelling of adjacent ground for a market garden may well have adversely affected drainage. However *Gagea lutea* is an intermittent flowerer and its leaves are very similar to those of young bluebells so there is still a chance it has been overlooked.

Masterwort (*Peucedanum ostruthium*) was, as its name implies, thought to be effective against a range of conditions. *Culpeper's Complete Herbal* (1653) recommends it as a cure for cold rheums, shortness of breath, expelling kidney stones, dropsy, cramps, poisoning, etc. Originally the only known site in VCs 86 and 87 was the small circular Kirk o' Muir graveyard (NS 7011 8399) by the side of Loch Carron. It may be there by design since herbs were thought to be more effective if grown on holy ground. The loss of the colony was only just prevented in 2008 when, thanks to the prompt cooperation of Stirling Council's Cemeteries Service, the strimmers were intercepted as they prepared the site for the annual service. As a result of the publicity given to this site a second colony was found in 2009 on the road verge 0.3 km west of the junction between the Cringate Muir and North Third reservoir roads NS 7476 8945.

Finds in Vice County 87

VC 87 (or West Perth) includes the western end of the combined Victorian Counties of Perthshire and Clackmannan as well as half the modern county of Stirlingshire. It covers the watershed to the north of the Forth from Loch Lomond in the west to Culross in the east. The BSBI recorders for the area are Liz Lavery (contact: lavery@carnbo.freeserve.co.uk) *and Paul Stanley.*

During a field excursion to Kippenrait Glen Special Area of Conservation a large colony of the rarer alternate-leaved species of golden saxifrage (*Chrysosplenium alternifolium*) was spotted in a boggy area 25 m west of the concrete footbridge across the River Allan (NS 7876 9903) This find was doubly interesting because in his *Herbarium Britannicum* (1804) the famous botanist George Don recorded '*Chrysosplenium alternifolium found in a deep shady den called Burn of old Wharry and another called Cox Burn'*. These two burns enter the Allan on either side of this site. He probably found the plant when apprenticed as a clockmaker in Dunblane during the 1780s (Morris, 1908). While examining these plants we became aware that town hall clock (*Adoxa moschatellina*) was growing at the edges of the colony as well as in the adjacent woodland and up the river bank. This diminutive plant has a single 5 cm flower stalk topped by a ball of five greenish flowers. Closer examination shows that there are four flowers arranged like the faces of a town hall clock each with ten anthers resembling the clock markings. The plant was described as '*A symbol of Christian watchfulness*' in the Reverend Keble Martin's *Concise British Flora*, which presumably signifies all-round vigilance. The fifth flower points upward and often only has four petals in the shape of a cross resulting in the alternative name 'Good Friday plant'.

The intensity and efficiency of modern agriculture has resulted in the local extinction of many field weeds. There have been no recent local records of the blue cornflower or corn cockle though both have been incorporated into wild meadow plantings. The corn marigold (*Chrysanthemum segetum*) was always considered the most noxious of cornfield weeds. In Handley's (1953) book on Scottish 18th century farming he states '*the gool or wild chrysanthemum was so widespread and did so much mischief that the peasants were forced to bestir themselves in order to keep it in check. Gool courts were established in many baronies for the purpose of inflicting fines on those that permitted the gool to flourish, culprits being summoned after the 'gool riding' or periodic inspection of the lands of the parish'*. These policies were obviously effective since it was described as rare in 1831 but corn marigold still fights on and in 2006 thousands of plants covered a large set-aside field on the Carse of Lecropt testifying to a viable seed bank still in the soil. The farmer obligingly allowed the plants to seed thereby replenishing the seed stock for future generations. There are a number of fields around Doune where patches of corn marigold spring up when missed by the sprayers. In 2008 they were recorded at Inverardoch Mains (NN 7295 0198), the field south of Black Park (NN 7295 0198) and in the field margins on both sides of the A820, 2 km east of the village (NN 7476 0111). The field west of Old Keir (NS 7623 9778) also contained Chicory (*Cichorium intybus*) with its distinctive pale blue flowers which was recorded in 1831 across the river in Cornton.

The construction of a new roundabout at Logie produced a spoil heap which became covered in a solid mass of weld or dyer's rocket (*Reseda luteola*) before it was grassed over. Forrest (1831) records weld's presence in the area long ago *'This plant is found in great abundance at the foot of Dumyat. It is used for dyeing woollen stuffs of a yellow colour'*. John Harrison a local historian could not shed any light on whether it was a crop in the area but found an account of 1637 in the Stirling Archives involving the purchase of several cart loads of wald and strae wald by a litster or dyster. Another introduced species *Reseda alba* was discovered growing in profusion in the remains of the mills at the base of Alva Glen.

While counting the northern marsh orchids (*Dactylorhiza purpurella* hybrids) on the A9 embankment just north of Lecropt Church (NS 7806 9816) a large colony (300 plants) of the rare diminutive adder's tongue fern (*Ophioglossum vulgatum*) was discovered. This tiny plant (3-8 cm) would probably not be recognised as a fern by most naturalists. Rather than having the highly divided leaves typical of most ferns it has a single frond which divides to produce a mouth-like sheathing oval leaf enclosing a tongue-like spike which carries the spores. Moonwort (*Botrychium lunaria*) which is a close relative, has its leaf fringed with half moons. The 17th century *Doctrine of the Signatures* decreed that all plants had been signed by the Creator with some physical clue of their medicinal properties. Adder's tongue fern's resemblance to a snake's open mouth and tongue defined it as useful for snakebites. Similarly mistletoe being one of the few plants to grow downwards was used to cure the 'falling down disease' - epilepsy. Some plants still retain names related to this strange herbal practice, for instance lesser celandine or pilewort (*Ranunculus ficaria*) has root tubers that resemble piles, lungwort (*Pulmonaria officinalis*) has leaves with spots on them that are supposed to look like diseased lungs.

In late July an excursion organised by Liz Lavery was run to square NN5124 at the top of Kirkton Glen above Balquhidder. This area includes the botanically-rich crags at the top of the pass (598 m) above and below Lochan an Eireannaich; a band of limestone outcrops here adding to the floral diversity. One of the objectives was to re-find records for *Gentianella campestris* (field gentian) for the BSBI Threatened Plants Project. This goal was easily achieved with good numbers on the crags. Growing with it on ledges and forming natural rock gardens, were *Saxifraga oppositifolia* (purple saxifrage), *Alchemilla alpina* (alpine lady's mantle), *Linum catharticum* (fairy flax), *Persicaria vivipara* (alpine bistort), *Potentilla crantzii* (alpine cinquefoil), *Silene acaulis* (moss campion) and *Polygala vulgaris* (common milkwort). On the same crags, but in flatter acid grassland, the shy flowering *Cornus suecica* (dwarf cornel) was found hiding under blaeberry (*Vaccinium myrtillus*). This member of the dogwood family was first recorded in Scotland in 1772 by John Lightfoot who wrote that the fruits *'had sweet and waterish taste and are supposed by Highlanders to create a great appetite'* apparently the Gaelic is lus-a-chraois, plant of gluttony. High above the main path the group found the bizarre fern *Botrychium lunaria* (see above). On the north side of the watershed looking down into Glen Dochart the rarest of our three mountain speedwells *Veronica fruticans* (rock speedwell) was found on what resembled a small area of tilted limestone pavement together with two or three plants of *Draba incana* (hoary whitlowgrass). In the bogs and stony flushes, particularly around the lochan, the lovely *Tofieldia pusilla* (Scottish asphodel) was growing together with *Equisetum variegatum* (variegated horsetail), *Juncus triglumis* (three-flowered rush), *Juncus alpinoarticulatus* (alpine rush) and *Saxifraga stellaris* (starry saxifrage). In total 130 species were recorded in this high-level 1 km square (Lavery, 2009).

References

Balfour, J.H. 1849. Plants in flower at the Bridge of Allan. *Botanical Gazette* 1, 136-137.

Blamey, M., Fitter, R. and Fitter, A. 2003. *Wild Flowers of Britain and Ireland*. London: A. and C. Black Ltd.

Croall, A. 1881. Remarks on the vegetation of the season. *Transactions of the Stirling Field Club* 4, 54-55.

Crockart, I.B. 1977. A note on Yellow Star of Bethlehem. *The Forth Naturalist and Historian* 2, 69-70.

Forrest, W.H. 1831. Report, chemical and medical, of Airthrey Mineral Springs: and a list of phaenogamous plants collected in the vicinity. Stirling 1831.

Gaywood, M. 2006. Natural heritage trends of Scotland: phenological indicators of climate change. Scottish Natural Heritage Commissioned Report 16, pp.37-8.

Gilmour, J. 1944. *British Botanists*. London: William Collins.

Handley, J.E. 1953. *Scottish Farming in the 18th Century*. London: Faber and Faber.

Lassiere, O. 1992. Tropical water fern Azolla filliculoides at Airthrey Loch, Stirling University. *The Forth Naturalist and Historian* 15, 55-57.

Lavery, E. 2008. Perthshire Society of Natural Science Botanical Section. Bulletin 31.

McDougall, G. 1882. Notes on local plants. *Transactions of Stirling Natural History and Archaeological Society* 5, 63-67

Morris, D.B. 1908. Some noteworthy local botanists *Transactions of the Stirling Natural History and Archaeological Society* 30, 66-85.

Roberts, A.M.I., Last, F.T. and Kempton, E. 2004. Preliminary analyses of changes in the first flowering dates of plants between 1978 and 2001. Scottish Natural Heritage Commissioned Report 035.

Sparks, T. and Collinson, N. 2003. Wildlife starts to adapt to a warming climate. *Biologist* 50, 273-6.

Figure 1. Female butterbur plants (*Petasites hybridus*) growing on the verge of the A811 near Kippen.

DUNBLANE WEATHER REPORT 2008

Neil Bielby

With the Parkhead semi-automatic weather station still apparently inoperative; this is an abridged version of a fuller local weather log compiled from data recorded in my suburban back garden at 56 Ochiltree, Dunblane. This is situated 50 metres to the east of the Dunblane Hydro ridge (100 metres a.s.l.) in a shallow, sheltered valley.

Daily rainfall, maximum and minimum temperatures, barometric pressure, cloud cover and wind direction and speed (Beaufort Scale) are recorded. All except the maximum daily temperature are taken at 09.00 h. (The period for 24 hour (daily) precipitation totals runs from 09.00 to 09.00). A brief description of the weather is also recorded along with exceptional and unusual weather phenomena across the UK (temperatures are meaned from two maximum/minimum thermometers situated at a height of one metre on the north wall of a detached, harled, brick garage).

All normals etc. refer to the last 14 years (1995-2008).

2008 – Overview

It was a little cooler and wetter than normal with the mean temperature of 8.26°C being 0.31°C below average while total precipitation of 1223.6 mm was 10 % above average. As usual there were seasonal variations with Winter (Dec-Feb) being warmer and wetter than usual the mean temperature being 0.26°C and precipitation 27 % above the norms. Spring (Mar-May), was slightly cooler (–0.16°C) and a little drier than average whilst it will come as no surprise that the Summer (Jun-Aug) was wetter (+33 %), but it was slightly warmer than usual. Autumn (Sep-Nov) was colder (–0.81°C) and drier (–15 %) than the norm. There were 67 air frosts, 13 above the mean, with as usual, December having the most with 20. Snow lay on the ground at 9am on ten mornings. Temperatures peaked at 26.7°C (28th July) whilst -8.9°C was the lowest recorded (30th Nov & 3rd Dec). Measurable precipitation (>0.1 mm) fell on 218 days, 11 above the norm, while the highest daily amount was 35 mm (25th Jan). Barometric pressure ranged from 965 mb to 1041 mb with the average of 1009 mb being 2 mb below the mean.

January was wet – very wet! The 265.4 mm recorded made it not only the wettest January but also the wettest month yet; easily surpassing the 219.4 mm of October 1998. This was double the average January rainfall and the 35 mm which fell on the 25th was the most on a single day for January and the 6th wettest day ever. Precipitation was recorded on 27 days, five more than the norm, and snow lay on three mornings. It was slightly milder than normal with the mean temperature of 2.86°C being 0.26°C above the norm. The average daily high was exactly the same as the long term norm but the nightly lows were 0.54°C below. Frosts were recorded on 12 days – one below the norm.

The average pressure of 1001 mb was 8 mb below the mean with a high of 1020 mb and a low of 979 mb.

Snow fell during the night of the 3rd/4th providing an accumulation of 8 cm (3 inches) of wet snow by 8.45am. Winds of up to 80 mph across central and southern Scotland on the 8th brought down trees, blew over lorries and caused the closure of the Tay, Forth, Erskine and Skye bridges: 20,000 homes were left without electricity (mostly in Argyll): 33.1 mm of rain fell in 24 hours. Heavy snow on the hills on the 10th and 11th followed by a settled, mostly sunny weekend, provided the best skiing at Scotland's resorts for many a winter. Prolonged sleet and heavy rain between the 23rd and 26th resulted in the R. Carron bursting its banks in Denny – resulting in the M80 being closed temporarily. Very strong winds on the 31st blew over a lorry on the Forth Road Bridge causing its closure for a time.

February was slightly warmer and drier than normal with the mean temperature of 3.68°C up 0.45°C on the average. Night minimum temperatures were +0.39°C and day maximums +0.52°C on the means. Precipitation of 77.8 mm was recorded (18.6 mm falling on the last day of the month) which was 26 % below the norm. Average air pressure of 1014 mb was 4 mb above the mean with the 1041 mb recorded on the 14th the highest ever for February. There were 14 air frosts; one above the mean, with a low of –4.7°C (2nd). No snow lay at 9am on any morning.

A deep depression crossing the Orkneys brought gale force westerly winds, gusting to 84 mph, across SW Scotland / NW England during the night of the 31st / 1st. These caused the trawler Spinningdale to run aground on St Kilda while further south, the Irish ferry Riverdance was washed ashore on Blackpool beach by a freak wave. Inland, 40-60 mph winds and heavy snow caused blizzard conditions over the high ground in Scotland although Dunblane only received the odd flurry. The A9 was closed between Blair Atholl and Drumochter during the 1st. As the belt of heavy snow worked its way down the east side of the UK, a 100 motorists were trapped overnight in their cars in Durham – mostly on the A66. A dry spell of 11 days from the 9th-19th, during which a high pressure system (1041 mb) prevailed, produced occasional dense fogs in the Carse of Stirling – some lasting all day. A remarkable 16°C was recorded at Tain on the 23rd (only 9.9°C in Dunblane). The 29th was particularly miserable, with driving rain all day on strong westerlies which reached 75 mph in Dumfries & Galloway: 18.6 mm of rain fell in Dunblane with Inveruglas receiving 64 mm. There was a marked east/west split during the final week of the month with the western highlands being battered by strong westerly winds and heavy rain – Inveruglas receiving 371 mm (14.6 inches) whereas the eastern coastal fringe of Scotland remained virtually dry.

March was colder and wetter than normal with a mean temperature of 3.84°C which was 1.07°C below average. Nights were 1.26°C and days 0.88°C colder. Precipitation was 27 % above the mean with the 97 mm recorded falling on 21 days – two more than the norm. Average barometric pressure of 998 mb was the lowest ever for March; 13 mb below the mean whilst the 965 mb recorded on the 10th also set a new low for the month. There were 15 air frosts, four more than average, with a low of –4.1°C (17th); the garden pond was frozen on eight mornings and snow lay on the ground on one.

There was a thin covering of snow on the morning of the 3rd but parts of Lanarkshire received up to 15 cm. A very deep low of 965 mb on the 10th (the second lowest barometric pressure recorded here after 964 mb on 25/12/99) coincided with equinoxal spring tides to produce storm surges on the SW & S coasts of England with winds of 95 mph recorded at the Needles on the Isle of Wight. A depression over Southern England (15th) brought 18 hours of rain resulting in the heaviest March downpour in 100 years in some places. Northerly winds brought an Arctic blast on the 21st/22nd causing the Glenshee and Lecht roads to be closed due to drifting snow as gusts of 80 mph were recorded at the latter ski centre.

April was colder and wetter than normal with the mean temperature of 6.62°C being 1.11°C below the average. The night mean low was –1.38°C and the daytime high –0.84°C of the average. Total precipitation of 81.6 mm was 32 % above the mean and was recorded on 20 days, 3 above the norm. The maximum daily high of 14.9°C was the lowest for April to date; the mean being 17.99 and the highest 22°C. There were seven air frosts, two more than the norm.

Pressure built to 1020 mb on the 3rd when warm air pulled up from the south raised temperatures to a year max of 14.9°C (18.9°C at Inverbervie, Kincardine-shire was the highest anywhere in the UK since 14th Oct the previous year). Cold northerly winds returned on the 5th although the day was mostly sunny. There was a thin covering of fluffy snow at 9am on the 6th with occasional snow flurries during the rest of the morning: bitter N 4-5 winds persisted all day and a low of –6°C was recorded at Warcop, Cumbria.

May was warmer and much drier than usual with the mean temperature of 12.46°C being 1.46°C above the norm making it the second warmest May after 2004 (mean of 12.7°C). Rainfall of 18.7 mm was the lowest ever for May – only 27 % of the norm and the second lowest for any month after the 18.4 mm recorded in August 1995. Measurable rainfall of more than 0.1 mm was recorded on nine days; only the sixth time the number has been in single figures for a month – the lowest being seven days in July 2000. It was the warmest May in Scotland since 1914 and the 4th driest ever, with only 34 % of the usual rainfall. The first ten days of May were the warmest for this period in 250 years of UK records.

High pressure persisted throughout most of the month being just strong enough to hold off the Atlantic fronts. Easterly winds dominated, depressing temperatures down the east coast whereas the west coast and islands basked in almost unbroken sunshine (Tiree recorded 15.9 hours on the 25th). In Dunblane, many days were typified by early haar / cloud being burnt off during the morning to give sunny afternoons and evenings.

June was slightly cooler and drier than average with the mean temperature of 13.55°C being 0.37°C below the norm. The mean night low was –0.82°C with the daytime high mean being +0.09°C above their norms. Total rainfall of 64.4 mm, which was recorded on 15 days, was 11 % below the monthly mean. The average pressure of 1011 mb was three below the mean with a peak of only 1019 mb.

Heavy rain during the evening/night of the 1st/2nd brought an end to the prolonged easterly airflow which had persisted throughout almost the whole of May. Light northerly winds and clear skies resulted in ground frosts as far south as London (16th/17th). On the evening of the 21st, a much heralded Atlantic depression arrived, producing 18.8 mm in 16 hours (54 mm at Keswick). It continued unsettled until the month end with Atlantic depressions and associated fronts. A very late frost of –2°C was recorded at Tulloch Bridge (24th).

July was a little warmer and wetter than usual with the mean temp of 16.4°C and rainfall of 90.8 mm being 0.5°C and 21 % above their norms respectively. The daytime high average of 21.15°C and the night-time low average of 11.7°C were +0.11°C and +0.94°C above their means.

The weather remained unsettled with rain most days. Walkers on Dartmoor had to be rescued after 104 mm of rain caused streams to rise dramatically (6th). Warm, humid weather saw temperatures peak at a monthly high of 26.7°C on the 28th (31°C London 27th). Torrential rain accompanied by an electric storm dumped 10 mm in only 10 minutes at 6pm on the 29th. More persistent rain with heavy pulses deposited 34.8 mm in 24 hours from 4pm on the 31st.

The **August** mean temperature was exactly the same as the average. However, the mean night low was 1°C above and the mean daily high 1°C below the norm. Total rainfall of 157.7 mm was the second highest to date for August (171.9 mm, 2004); 92 % above average, with measurable amounts recorded on 23 days. The average pressure of 1007 mb was the lowest ever for this month. Most of the UK (apart from Northern Scotland) experienced the second dullest August on record, with only 1912 having less sunshine.

The weather continued unsettled with sunshine and showers. It started raining at 9pm on the evening of the 5th and continued until noon on the 7th by which time 47.4 mm had fallen. The temperature struggled to 12.1°C on the 6th (the lowest to date for August), during which, a raw east wind blew, making it feel more like winter. The 9am to 9am total rainfall of 33.7 mm made it the ninth wettest 'day' ever. There was 28 hours respite before another Atlantic front raced into Britain on the 9th. The rain started at c.6am and was steady to light during the day but torrential downpours during the evening and night resulted in a 24 hour total of 22 mm. 70.8 mm fell during the week (Sun.-Sat.) making it the wettest yet for summer and the 15th wettest ever. The weather continued unsettled as regular Atlantic fronts worked their way up and across the UK. Fife was badly affected by flooding towards the month end. Eskdalemuir recorded only 23 hours of sunshine between the 1st-19th August.

September was drier than normal with the 73.2 mm of rain recorded being 84 % of the norm. Mean temperatures were almost identical to the normals.

An autumnal chill was in the air when the temperature dropping to 3.9°C on the 5th (–2°C Braemar).There was serious flooding in the West Country and South Wales (5th) with the 185 mm (7.28 in) which fell at Ponsticill in the Brecon Beacons being the highest 24 hour total anywhere in the UK since the Boscastle floods in 2004. These rains and resultant floods transferred to Northumberland the following day, depositing c.100 mm in 48 hours. The weather settled down as barometric pressure rose steadily to reach 1038 mb by the 26th resulting in a late Indian summer with seven consecutive dry days and much sunshine.

October was colder and wetter than usual with the mean temperature of 6.71°C being 1.75°C below average. This made it the 2nd coldest October in 14 years after 2003, whose mean was 6.57°C. There were seven air frosts. It was 14 % wetter than normal with 159.4 mm making it the 16th wettest month ever but only the seventh wettest October. Precipitation was recorded on 22 days – equal to the mean, and the average pressure of 1008 mb was also the same as the mean.

The first frost of the winter (–0.1°C) was recorded on the 2nd with –2.1°C on the 5th. A succession of Atlantic lows – the remnants of North American hurricanes – then deposited 61.6 mm in five days (6th-10th). A daytime high of 23°C in Berkshire was the warmest for this time of year since 1978. Daily amounts of rainfall increased substantially from the 19th with 80.4 mm falling in eight days. This was accompanied by strong winds which occasionally caused Scotland's main bridges to be closed to high sided vehicles: gusts of 77 mph were recorded in the Outer Hebrides (25th). The Lake District marathon was cancelled on the 25th when 81 mm of rain fell in 24 hours and the weekly total at Shap was 223 mm. A cold northerly airflow developed from the 27th, persisting to the month end. This produced nightly frosts with a minimum of –3.8°C (28th) but also plenty of sunshine. There were substantial snowfalls in the north and north-east of Scotland on the 28th/29th which caused the Lecht and Glenshee passes to be temporarily closed. Up to 7 cm of snow lay on the Chilterns and the temperature plummeted to –7°C at Topcliffe, N. Yorks (29th). On the same day, a phenomenal hailstorm (78 mm), struck SE Devon causing serious flooding in the Otter Valley and Southern England received its first significant October snowfall since 1926.

November was colder and drier than usual with a mean temperature of 4.09°C; 0.63°C below the average. The –8.9°C recorded at 9am on the 30th was the lowest ever for November and with the temperature only reaching –4°C during that day, it was also the lowest ever daytime max. for this month. There were 12 air frosts, four above the mean. The 50.6 mm of precipitation was only 48 % of the monthly average making it the second driest after 47.4 mm in 2004.

The cold snap continued for the first four days of the month with a minimum of –4.8°C (3rd). The 2nd and 3rd were perfect winter days of unbroken sunshine. The first measurable rain in 10 days fell on the 6th with more or less continuous rain for the following two days. A southwesterly airflow brought unusually mild air from sub-tropical latitudes on the 13th/14th raising temperatures to 12.3°C on the 14th (16°C in other parts of eastern Scotland). A north-westerly, then northerly airflow, brought bitter Arctic air from the 21st to the 23rd. The north and north east coasts were hit with frequent heavy snow showers which blocked the Lecht, Glenshee and Cairn O' Mount passes. Up to 25 cm fell on the Yorkshire Wolds (22nd). An Atlantic depression (991 mb) deposited 2 cm of snow as it hit the cold air mass over the country during the night of the 22nd/23rd. Frosts for the next couple of nights (–2.9°C) as pressure built to 1021 mb, helped retain patches of snow until an Atlantic front passed from N-S over Scotland during the night of the 26th/27th depositing 8.5 mm of rain. The Arctic air flow resumed on the 28th bringing with it night frosts and temperatures plunged to an all time November low of –8.9°C on the 30th (–12°C Braemar) when the daytime temperature struggled to only –4°C. In compensation, the days were sunny, except for parts of the Carse of Stirling, where dense fog lingered for most of the day on the 29th and 30th.

December was colder and drier than normal with the mean temperature of 1.3°C being 1°C below the average. There were 20 air frosts, equal to the most ever for the month, with the garden pond being frozen on 16 days. Snow lay at 9am on five mornings. Rainfall, at 87 mm, was 85 % of the norm.

The cold snap continued with nightly frosts, again plunging to –8.9°C on the 3rd, (–13°C at Tulloch Br. (4th)) when the daytime temperature only reached –4.1°C. Pressure dropped rapidly to 975 mb during the night of the 2nd / 3rd as a deep Atlantic low moved across the country depositing 10 mm of precipitation-snow turning to sleet then rain. The North Yorkshire Moors were most badly affected with roads impassable and 6,000 homes in the area were left without power. However, days were mostly sunny and calm and the first week in December was the coldest in ten years and the sunniest in 25 years for the UK as a whole. Pressure dropped rapidly to 985 mb on the 13th with Shetland experiencing storm force ten southerly gales. The weather continued unsettled and progressively mild as successive Atlantic weather systems affected the country. A total of 45.3 mm fell between the 16th and 20th causing flooding in low lying areas. The 21st was another windy day with the south-westerlies gusting to force seven and reaching 75 mph on Shetland. The weather then settled as high pressure built over the country reaching 1041 mb on the 26th. There were night frosts from the 26th with the temperature remaining below freezing all day on the 31st.

Table 1. Temperature and precipitation 2008. N. Bielby Climatological Station Dunblane.

	Temp Mean maxima	Temp Mean minima	Number of Air Frosts	Total precipitation (mm)	Greatest 24 hour total (mm)	Number of days of measurable rain
January	4.8 (4.8/6.5)	1.0 (0.4/0.5)	12 (14/13)	265.4 (128.7/110.7)	35.0 (35.0)	27 (21)
February	6.6 (6.1/6.9)	0.8 (0.4/0.8)	14 (13/11)	77.8 (104.8/73.2)	18.6 (38.0)	16 (18)
March	7.7 (8.6/9.1)	0.0 (1.3/1.9)	15 (11/7)	97.0 (76.5/81.4)	12.5 (30.5)	21 (16)
April	11.4 (12.2/11.8)	1.9 (3.3/3.4)	7 (5/4)	81.6 (61.9/47.5)	13.0 (27.8)	20 (15)
May	15.9 (16.2/15.3)	5.5 (5.8/5.8)	0 (2/1)	18.7 (68.5/56.9)	9.3 (27.1)	9 (17)
June	19.1 (19.0/17.7)	8.0 (8.8/8.4)	0 (0/ <1)	64.4 (77.9/57.1)	18.8 (28.0)	15 (15)
July	21.1 (21.0/19.8)	11.7 (10.8/10.6)	0 (0/0)	90.8 (75.0/62.9)	24.0 (33.5)	19 (15)
August	19.2 (20.2/19.4)	11.6 (10.6/10.2)	0 (0/0)	157.7 (82.3/68.1)	33.7 (35.4)	23 (14)
September	16.0 (16.0/16.3)	8.2 (8.3/8.3)	0 (<1/<1)	73.2 (86.6/87.7)	19.0 (36.5)	16 (17)
October	10.5 (11.7/12.9)	2.9 (5.2/5.4)	7 (3/2)	159.4 (139.3/ 97.9)	21.3 (41.9)	22 (22)
November	6.6 (7.4/9.2)	1.6 (2.0/2.6)	12 (8/8)	50.6 (105.6/98.9)	10.0 (39.0)	14 (20)
December	3.5 (4.3/7.2)	-0.9 (0.3/1.1)	20 (14/11)	87.0 (102.0/101.0)	17.0 (26.8)	16 (19)
Year (2008)	12.0 (12.3/13.2)	4.5 (4.9/5.3)	67 (54)	1224 (1109/943)	35 (41.9)	218 (207)

The Climatological Normals Dunblane/Parkhead are shown in ( ). Figure in parenthesis in the 'Greatest 24 hour total (mm)' refer to the highest figure for that month. Temperatures are given in degrees Celsius.

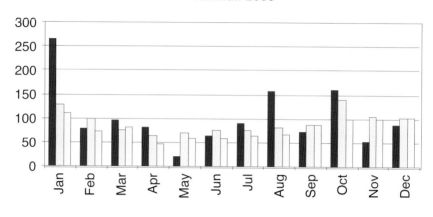

Figure 1. Rainfall 2008.

THE STATUS OF ARCTIC CHARR *SALVELINUS ALPINUS* IN THE FORTH CATCHMENT

Peter S. Maitland

Introduction

The Arctic charr is the most northerly freshwater fish in the world, occurring in lakes across parts of Britain and Ireland where it was previously described as 15 separate species. Most authorities now agree that all these stocks belong to a single polymorphic species complex *Salvelinus alpinus* (L.) – though recently Kottelat and Freyhof (2007) have attempted to resurrect the original species. This fish was given little protection in British and Irish law until recently and there has been a gradual loss of natural populations in all the countries concerned. A few new stocks have been created either intentionally or accidentally. In Scotland, only a small proportion of the recorded natural populations has been studied and many of these are now extinct. There are at least four introduced populations in Scotland originating from native Scottish stocks, but the fate of stocks introduced from Canada for aquaculture is uncertain.

A century ago, Regan (1911) was concerned about the future of Arctic charr: 'it is certain that if Char were to die out in the next few thousand years at the same rate as they have done in the last century they would remain only in a very few lakes in the British Isles.' Previously, Harvie-Brown and Buckley (1887) suggested that 'It may be of scientific interest to catalogue all the lochs known to contain charr, against such as have never yielded any to anglers. Such a list might be useful in the future.' However, although Hardie (1940) started such a list it was not until 1970 that a preliminary list of the charr lochs of Scotland was produced by the author (Maitland, 1983), including those in which the species has become extinct – the latter component becoming longer each decade.

In Britain and Ireland, the Arctic charr populations in most lakes have been isolated from each other for thousands of years and have developed a variety of phenotypic characteristics (Gunther, 1865; Day, 1887; Regan, 1914) which are probably genetically based (Child, 1977; Ferguson, 1981; Hartley *et al.*. 1992; Adams *et al.*, 2007). Maxwell (1919) expressed it colloquially:'... one of the most conspicuous survivals of the reign of ice in our islands; a slowly vanishing race, still maintaining existence in a few scattered and profound meres and lakes. ... their strict segregation for thousands of years, prohibiting all admixture of different colonies, are quite enough to account for some variation in colour, form, and even structure among fish of a single species inhabiting widely separate sheets of water.'

The author has previously reviewed the status of Arctic charr in southern Scotland (Maitland, 1992). The objective of this paper is to review populations of this species in the Forth catchment and explore the reasons for the success or the demise of populations there.

Arctic charr

The Arctic charr occurs all round the northern hemisphere and in the most northerly parts of its range forms mixed seagoing and non-seagoing populations where the seagoing charr can reach a large size. Although they must have done so thousands of years ago, none of the populations of Arctic charr in Scotland migrate to the sea and so the adults are much smaller than in places where they do (i.e northern Norway, Iceland, Greenland and Canada). The adults vary in size in different lochs but are typically about 20-25 cm in length (85-170 g in weight). However, in some lochs they may regularly reach over 35 cm and 600 g. Some exceptionally large charr have been recorded recently from the vicinity of floating fish farm cages in Scottish lochs where their diet is boosted by the large amounts of waste food pellets available to them.

Although occurring quite widely in Ireland and northern Scotland, and very locally in south west Scotland, north west England and north Wales, the Arctic charr is not a familiar fish to most people and when encountered is often regarded as a curiosity – 'an Ice Age relict'. In fact, it occurs in quite large numbers in some lochs, probably outnumbering the brown trout *Salmo trutta* population where they co-exist, as they usually do. However, due to its cryptic habits it is seldom seen, even by anglers. There has been considerable interest in the species in recent years and it is now being studied and angled for in several waters. In other parts of the charr's range it is considered to be a most valuable fish for consumption by both humans and dogs.

Compared to many other parts of the northern hemisphere, Arctic charr have been relatively little exploited by humans in Scotland. Malloch (1910) noted that 'Altogether it is a very beautiful fish. Little use is made of them in Scotland, although they are excellent for the table.' Though it is well known that in the English Lake District fish were caught and used as a basis for a small scale local luxury food, much less has been published about the situation in Scotland where, however, they were also important locally and indeed potted, as they were further south. Most fish were harvested at their spawning time, when they are most vulnerable, and sold locally. In Sutherland, Arctic charr were netted in the 1700s and salted in barrels for the winter as what was called 'freshwater herring.'

Information sources

Although there are many historical references to the fish fauna of Scotland, because of its cryptics habits, very few of them refer to Arctic charr. Two main exceptions to this are The Statistical Accounts of Scotland – Old (Sinclair, 1791) and New (Gordon, 1845) – and the Ordnance Gazetteer of Scotland (Groome, 1882). These two publications, together with a few others which deal with specific geographic areas or sites, for example Loch Leven (Burns-Begg, 1874), are the only option to gaining an insight into the changing status of Arctic charr in Scotland over the last three centuries (Maitland, 1977). The bathymetry and other details of many of the lochs occupied by Arctic charr are available from the classical surveys of Murray and Pullar (1910).

The Statistical Account of Scotland (Sinclair, 1791) is a compilation of accounts by the ministers of all the Scottish parishes and most include details of the natural history and fisheries of each parish. The geographic coverage of Scotland is comprehensive, but the accounts vary as to the quality of information given on fish – especially the less obvious species. The New Statistical Account of Scotland (Gordon, 1845) is less useful generally as far as fish are concerned. More useful, however, is the Ordnance Gazetteer of Scotland (Groome, 1882) which covers all the major lochs and rivers in Scotland, providing a great deal of information on their fish.

All the information from these sources together with other information and records available to the author have been catalogued below by year for each of the larger lochs in the Forth catchment which are likely to have held Arctic charr in the past.

The spellings of 'char' or 'charr' for this species are both acceptable, but the latter – derived from the Gaelic 'tarr' meaning belly (one Gaelic name for the charr is Tarrdhearg, meaning red bellied) – is the more authentic (Morton, 1955). Several common names and their variants have been used locally in Scotland in the past, e.g. Alpine charr, cuddy, gelletroch, jar, red-bellied trout, red waimb, and some of these appear in the references which are reviewed below.

The Forth catchment

The larger lochs of the upper Forth catchment and their inter-connections, may be represented in diagrammatic form thus:

Actual details of each loch are given below along with available information on the known status of Arctic charr there.

Loch Doine, Forth (Teith), NGR: 2470 7192, Altitude: 126.3 m; Maximum Depth: 19.8 m; Mean Depth: 10.1 m; Surface Area: 54 ha; Catchment Area: 9,971 ha (Murray and Pullar, 1910).

1793. 'These lakes (Doine, Voil, Lubnaig) and rivers abound in common-trout, bull-trout and jar, all of an excellent quality. ... The trout is in greatest perfection in April and May; the jar in August.' (Stewart, 1793).

1837. 'Our lakes, and rivers, and mountain streams, abound in trout, salmon, pike, eel, perch, char and other small fish.' (Robertson, 1837). Mentions 'Doin, Veoil and Lubnaig'.

1907. '1906. June. Two or three small char just near the head of Loch Doine.' (R.P. Hardie, unpublished notes).

1925. 'Char of 1/3 or 1/2 lb caught.' (in litt. E.L. Smith, September, 1925).

1958. 'Five charr received and analysed.' (G.F. Friend, unpublished notes).

1979. Arctic charr caught by anglers (Maitland *et al.,* 1984).

1984. Arctic charr (350) netted by Barbour (1984).

1997. Arctic charr netted by Alexander and Adams (1999, 2000).

2002. Arctic charr (14) netted by Colin Bull (personal communication, 2008). Also brown trout (5).

Loch Voil, Forth (Teith), NGR: 2505 7198, Altitude: 126.3 m; Maximum Depth: 29.9 m; Mean Depth: 12.5 m; Surface Area: 228 ha; Catchment Area: 9,971 ha (Murray and Pullar, 1910).

1793. 'These lakes (Doine, Voil, Lubnaig) and river abound in common-trout, bull-trout and jar, all of an excellent quality. ... The trout is in greatest perfection in April and May; the jar in August.' (Stewart, 1793).

1837. 'Our lakes, and rivers, and mountain streams, abound in trout, salmon, pike, eel, perch, char and other small fish.' (Robertson, 1837). Mentions 'Doin, Veoil and Lubnaig'.

1956. 'Five charr caught in stormy conditions at west end of Loch Voil under isthmus tree belt; July 1956. Two at least had *Henneguya* cysts.' (G.F. Friend, unpublished notes).

1970s. Arctic charr caught by anglers (Maitland *et al.,* 1984).

1992. Arctic charr angled (personal communication J. Alexander, 1992).

1997. Arctic charr netted by Alexander and Adams (1999, 2000).

2002. Arctic charr (5) netted by Colin Bull (personal communication, 2008). Also brown trout (7) and minnows *Phoxinus phoxinus* (8).

Loch Lubnaig, Forth (Teith), NGR: 2582 7134, Altitude: 123.5 m; Maximum Depth: 44.5 m; Mean Depth: 13.1 m; Surface Area: 249 ha; Catchment Area: 19,036 ha (Murray and Pullar, 1910).

1723. 'Loch Lubnack ... produces of fishes rid weams, trouts and some salmond.' (Macfarlane, 1723).

1724. 'The loch called Loch Loubnack ... abounds with trouts and has a kind of trout about the bigness of a herring called red wyms from the redness of their bellies and have whyt fins.' (Macfarlane, 1724).

1793. 'These lakes (Doine, Voil, Lubnaig) and river abound in common-trout, bull-trout and jar, all of an excellent quality. ... The trout is in greatest perfection in April and May; the jar in August.' (Stewart, 1793).

1794. 'Charr have been discovered in Lochlubnaig, and, when pickled, are found equal any from the lakes of the north of England. They live in the bottom of deep waters, and cannot easily be caught, without the seine or net. The English char have two rows of spots upon their sides; those of Lochlubnaig only one. They are also found in some other lakes in the neighbourhood.' (Robertson, 1794).

1837. 'Our lakes, and rivers, and mountain streams, abound in trout, salmon, pike, eel, perch, char and other small fish.' (Robertson, 1837). Mentions 'Doin, Veoil and Lubnaig'.

1847. 'In Lochs Katrine and Lubnaig there are a few charr.' (Stoddart, 1847).

1905. 'Supposed to be found only in Loch Lubnaig.' (Forbes, 1905).

1914. 'Charr reported by W.J.M. Menzies in 1914.' (R.P. Hardie, unpublished notes).

1960s. Arctic charr reported by J.F. Flannagan (1961), P.S. Maitland (1966), D. Biggart (1967) and J. Spittal (1967).

1977. Arctic charr caught by anglers (Maitland *et al.*, 1984).

1997. Arctic charr netted by Alexander and Adams (1999, 2000).

2002. Arctic charr (13) netted by Colin Bull (personal communication, 2008). Also brown trout (25), perch (3), minnows (12).

2002. 'I had a few charr from Loch Lubnaig last year, I think it was April. I was fishing the bottom from the bank with some grubs.' Internet posting, January, 2003).

2008. 'Marcus Tripney from Grangemouth caught a large perch (2 lb. 14 oz.) in Loch Lubnaig. Removing the size 14 hook and maggot from its mouth, a small Arctic charr was found at the back of its throat.' (Daily Record, June 13, 2008).

Loch Katrine, Forth, NGR: 2043 7509, Altitude: 110.9 m; Maximum Depth: 150.9 m; Mean Depth: 60.7 m; Surface Area: 1230.3 ha; Catchment Area: 11,093 ha (Murray and Pullar, 1910).

1724. 'Loch Katrine ... hath plenty of trout in it particularly Redwyms.' (Macfarlane, 1724).

1793. 'Loch Ketterin, Loch Con and Loch Ard ... These lakes abound with eel, pike and trout, all esteemed excellent in their kinds.' (Graham, 1793).

1837. 'Our lakes, and rivers, and mountain streams, abound in trout, salmon, pike, eel, perch, char and other small fish.' (Robertson, 1837). Mentions 'Catharine, Achray and Venachoir'.

1843. 'In Loch Katrine alone, the *Salmo Alpinus* or charr is to be found.' (Graham, 1843).

1847. 'In Lochs Katrine and Lubnaig there are a few charr,' (Stoddart, 1847).

1881. 'First proposed in 1855, the scheme to supply water to Glasgow was completed in 1881. It allowed the surface level of Loch Katrine to be raised by 4 feet or lowered by 3 feet, allowing a range of 7 feet. The subsequent control of Loch Arklet, diverting its water to Loch Katrine, added a further 1381 ha to its catchment.' (Murray and Pullar, 1910).

1882. 'It contains some char, abundance of good trout, and pike running up to 20 lbs.' (Groome, 1882).

1995. No Arctic charr caught in netting by W. Duncan (personal communication, 2008).

2002. No Arctic charr netted by Colin Bull (personal communication, 2008). Some brown trout (26), and pike (5).

Loch Achray, Forth, NGR: 2515 7064, Altitude: 84.2 m; Maximum Depth: 29.6 m; Mean Depth: 11 m; Surface Area: 83 ha; Catchment Area: 11,534 ha (Murray and Pullar, 1910).

1794. '... large pikes in Loch Vennachoir and Loch Achray, which are enemies to other fish.' (Robertson ,1794).

1837. 'Our lakes, and rivers, and mountain streams, abound in trout, salmon, pike, eel, perch, char and other small fish.' (Robertson, 1837). Mentions 'Catharine, Achray and Venachoir'.

1882. '... the fishing (trout, salmon-trout, pike and perch) is good and open to the public.' (Groome, 1882).

1940. 'Loch Achray has some char.' (Hardie, 1940).

1974. No Arctic charr caught in netting by the Freshwater Fisheries Laboratory (Maitland *et al.*, 1984).

1997. No Arctic charr caught in netting by Alexander and Adams (1999, 2000).

2002. No Arctic charr netted by Colin Bull (personal communication, 2008). Some perch (27), and pike (5).

Loch Venachar, Forth, NGR: 2570 7054, Altitude: 82.4 m; Maximum Depth: 33.9 m; Mean Depth: 12.9 m; Surface Area: 417 ha; Catchment Area: 19,518 ha (Murray and Pullar, 1910).

1794. '... large pikes in Loch Vennachoir and Loch Achray, which are enemies to other fish.' (Robertson, 1794).

1837. 'Our lakes, and rivers, and mountain streams, abound in trout, salmon, pike, eel, perch, char and other small fish.' (Robertson, 1837). Mentions 'Catharine, Achray and Venachoir'.

1882. 'Its waters contain some salmon, very fine trout, perch and large pike.' (Groome, 1882).

1974. No Arctic charr in netting by the Freshwater Fisheries Laboratory (Maitland *et al.,* 1984).

1997. No Arctic charr in netting by Alexander and Adams (1999, 2000).

2002. No Arctic charr netted by Colin Bull (personal communication, 2008). Some brown trout (2), and perch (124).

Loch Chon, Forth, NGR: 24217052, Altitude: 90.2 m; Maximum Depth: 22.9 m; Mean Depth: 8.9 m; Surface Area: 111.4 ha; Catchment Area: 1,618 ha (Murray and Pullar, 1910).

1793. 'Loch Ketterin, Loch Con and Loch Ard ... These lakes abound with eel, pike and trout, all esteemed excellent in their kinds.' (Graham, 1793).

1843. 'The fishes in the lakes and rivers are trout, pike, perch and eel. ... The trout of Loch-ard and Loch-con, which weigh from one to three pounds, are of the same quality with those of Loch Leven.' (Graham, 1843).

2002. No Arctic charr netted by Colin Bull (personal communication, 2008). Some perch (16), and pike (4).

Loch Ard, Forth, NGR: 2467 7017, Altitude: 32.0 m; Maximum Depth: 32.6 m; Mean Depth: 13.4 m; Surface Area: 243.5 ha; Catchment Area: 2,525 ha (Murray and Pullar, 1910).

1793. 'Loch Ketterin, Loch Con and Loch Ard ... These lakes abound with eel, pike and trout, all esteemed excellent in their kinds.' (Graham ,1793).

1843. 'The fishes in the lakes and rivers are trout, pike, perch and eel. ... The trout of Loch-ard and Loch-con, which weigh from one to three pounds, are of the same quality with those of Loch Leven.' (Graham ,1843).

1882. Loch Ard. 'The trout average 3/4 lb ... likewise there are pike of from 15 to 20 lbs.' (Groome, 1882).

2002. No Arctic charr netted by Colin Bull (personal communication, 2008). Some brown trout (7), perch (57), pike (1), and roach *Rutilus rutilus* (2).

Loch of Menteith, Forth, NGR: 2578 7006, Altitude: 16.8 m; Maximum Depth: 23.5 m; Mean Depth: 6.0 m; Surface Area: 264.2 ha; Catchment Area: 1,684 ha (Murray and Pullar, 1910).

The Loch of Menteith is the only natural expanse of water in Scotland usually to be called a lake. Known as the Loch of Menteith until the 19th century, its modern name may be a Victorian affectation reflecting its 'English' parkland setting.

1792. 'The Loch of Monteith ... abounds with perch, pike and eel, and affords some large trout.' (Stirling, 1792).

1843. 'The Lake of Inchmahome contains a variety of fish. The staple is the perch ... the lake has trout also ... pike ... eels. Salmon are said to have come into the lake before the erection of mills on the Guidie.' (Anonymous, 1843a).

1882. 'The trout fishing is ruined by the pike.' (Groome, 1882).

Loch Leven, Leven, NGR: 3149 7013, Altitude: 106.8 m; Maximum Depth: 25.3 m; Mean Depth: 4.5 m; Surface Area: 1,374 ha; Catchment Area: 13,193 ha (Murray and Pullar, 1910).

1629. 'In this lough is fish every day in the year gotten for store, none in Britain like, and consider the bigness of it, as also for fowl. .... The general kind of fishes be these – the pikes of which many as big as a man, eels, gelletoughes, chars, perches, camdowes (a kind of trout which have not scales), grey trouts. Gelletough is the he char, sysbinge the she. There is a river they call the Leven running out of it 8 miles into the sea, and in it is salmons. They dry them in their chimneys like red herring.' (Lowther, 1629).

1710. 'Loch Leven abounds with fine fish, such as salmon taken in summer. The gelletroch is a red-womb trout; it hath a small head; it is usually 18 inches long. The speckled trout, red-womb with white fins, taken in October with nets. Some are reddish within, some whitish. The grey trout, or bill-trout, some of them as big as a salmond, grayish skinn'd and red fish'd, a foot long, taken all the year over. Cendue or Camdue, in Irish, (Cean-dubh) blackhead, having a black spot on the top of its head; is fat, big as a Dunbar-herring, red-fish'd, much esteemed. Big eels and pearches in abundance.' (Sibbald, 1710).

1769. 'The fish of this loch are Pike, small perch fine eels and most excellent trouts: the best and the reddest I ever saw: the largest about six pounds in weight. The fishermen gave me an account of a species they called the gelly trout, which are only caught from October to January: are split, salted and dried for winter provision: by the description they were certainly our char, only of a larger size than we have in England or Wales, some being two feet and a half long.' (Pennant, 1769).

1793. 'The gally-trough, or char, abounds in the loch. The description of this fish is generally well known. What is remarkable of them is the size to which they often grow, some of them weighing near 2 lb., and they are never known to rise to a fly, or be caught with a hook baited in any way whatever.' (Smith, 1793).

1830. 'In the month of December of that year, the lake was reduced to three-fourths of its original extent, or to 3543 acres, by the completion of an extensive drainage scheme ... The top of the permanent spill-water at the sluice was, in terms of the Act, exactly four and a half feet below a mark indicating the original level, ...' (Burns-Begg, 1874).

1837. 'The very 'last of the race' is believed to have been caught with the net in the latter part of the season of 1837.' (Burns-Begg, 1874).

1839. 'It is much to be feared that one of the effects of the late partial drainage of the lake, has been the destruction of some of the species of the fish ... Certain of the sorts now seem to be extinct, and the char, *Salmo alpinus*, one of the finest fishes of the loch, has almost disappeared.' Put down by experts to: 1. Curtailment of loch area, 2. Strong currents at the new sluices, 3. Barrenness of new margin. (Buchanan, 1839).

1843. Sir William Jardine and Mr Wilson made in the course of two days' fishing in Lochleven attempts to find 'the missing and delicate charr or gelly-trough' but these attempts proved utterly unsuccessful. (Anonymous, 1843b).

1874. 'For some cause, which has never satisfactorily been ascertained, the charr has for a considerable number of years entirely disappeared from Lochleven, not a single specimen having been caught either with rod or net for upwards of thirty years.' (Burns-Begg, 1874).

Extinctions

It seems likely from the connectivity and geomorphology of the larger Trossachs lochs that all of those reviewed above are likely to have had populations of Arctic charr at one time. Why this fish should have become extinct in some lochs but not others is uncertain but some clues are available (Table 1).

Table 1. Factors relevant to the success or demise of Arctic charr in lochs in the Forth catchment. Those marked * have some water >100 feet deep.

Forth Lochs	% of loch <50 feet deep	% of loch >50 feet deep	Engineering Works	Pike present	Perch present
Doine	65	35	-	-	-
Voil	59	41	-	-	-
Lubnaig	65	35*	-	-	+
Katrine	18	82*	+	+	-
Ard	65	35*	-	+	+
Menteith	95	5	-	+	+
Chon	89	11	-	+	+
Achray	69	31	-	+	+
Venachar	62	38*	+	+	+
Leven	96	4	+	+	+

Factors critical to the success of populations of Arctic charr are believed to be the extent of available deep cool water, the impact of engineering works and the presence of predatory pike and perch.

Water depth is thought to be important to Arctic charr in providing both cool water during hot weather and a physical refuge from predators at all times. In spite of stratification, small bodies of deep water will warm up faster in summer than large ones. With the onset of a thermocline in summer, Arctic charr may be affected if the oxygen levels in deep water drop too low – a significant risk in eutrophic lochs such as Leven and Menteith. Where the area of deep water is small in relation to the shallow water habitat around it, which is suitable for predators, predation may be significant, especially at spawning time.

Engineering works which modify aquatic systems can affect Arctic charr in various ways. Significant drawdown, especially where it is permanent, can reduce the area of deep water available as well as exposing all spawning sites and leaving fish with nowhere to spawn until the new shoreline re-adjusts to provide clean gravels. Thus, it is not surprising that the Arctic charr population in Loch Leven became extinct a few years after the loch level was drawn down by 1.3 m – remembering that the present mean depth of the loch is just 4.5 m. Where hydro-dams have created fluctuating water levels Arctic charr usually seem able to cope and indeed may do better than brown trout there. Some new reservoirs have provided good habitat for Arctic charr and there are several new stocks of this species in other parts of Scotland where they have been introduced (Talla Reservoir) or gained access accidentally (Cruachan Reservoir).

Arctic charr are preyed on by other fish, notably by large ferox brown trout, with which they normally co-exist (Hardie, 1940), as well as pike and perch. It appears also that benthic piscivorous charr may also be significant predators of young charr in some habitats (Fraser *et al.,* 1998). Brown trout and eels *Anguilla anguilla* take the eggs of spawning charr – in Loch Doon the author found that the stomachs of all the brown trout caught along with spawning Arctic charr were full of charr eggs. Arctic charr seem particularly susceptible to predation by pike, a recent alien species in many charr waters, and a number of charr populations may have become extinct following the introduction of this voracious species, which is still being thoughtlessly moved about by humans.

Thus, in some waters, predatory fish may have a significant effect. Although pike are known occasionally to co-exist with Arctic charr and other salmonids (e.g. in Windermere), they have eliminated salmonids from other waters, for example Loch Choin in Perthshire (Munro, 1957). Many Scottish lochs, where pike and perch are the only species present now, are likely to have been occupied by brown trout (and in some cases Arctic charr) before pike and perch reached them by natural dispersal or introduction by humans. Arctic charr are particularly vulnerable to such large predators at spawning time in shallow water – unlike brown trout, which move into running water to spawn.

Other factors may be involved to some extent but it would appear that, in the Forth catchment at least, lochs with little deep water, some impact from engineering works and populations of pike and perch are most likely to have lost their populations of Arctic charr. Lochs Chon, Menteith and Leven, in particular, fall into this category. Conversely, Lochs Doine, Voil and Lubnaig, which have significant areas of deep water, little impact from engineering works and no pike seem to have retained their populations of Arctic charr for thousands of years.

Several other human impacts are believed to be involved in the extinction of populations of Arctic charr in Scotland and elsewhere (Maitland, 1995) and these include pollution, eutrophication, acidification (Loch Grannoch), afforestation, exploitation (St Mary's Loch), aquaculture, introductions and climate change. Afforestation in particular is known to have impacted significantly on waters in the Trossachs area (Harriman and Morrison, 1982). Much research remains to be done and unique stocks of this valuable species will continue to be lost unless positive action is taken through local conservation management backed by appropriate national legislation.

The status of Arctic charr at Loch Katrine is uncertain and more research work is needed here. Although it is affected by engineering works to provide water for the City of Glasgow, and pike are present, the loch is a very large one with extensive areas of deep water – 69 % of the loch is deeper than 100 feet, 47 % deeper than 200 feet, 30 % deeper than 300 feet and 17 % deeper than 400 feet (Murray and Pullar, 1910). Water level fluctuations due to abstraction are relatively small and pike habitat restricted. Recent netting for Arctic charr has been very limited and it seems quite likely that a population may still exist there.

Discussion

The conclusions from this review are that, although Arctic charr may have occurred in at least ten lochs in the Forth catchment in the past, there are now just three lochs (Doine, Voil and Lubnaig) with established populations. charr have definitely disappeared from three lochs (Leven, Achray and Venachar) and possibly from a fourth Katrine). Its past occurrence in three other lochs (Chon, Ard and Menteith) is likely but not certain and clearly none are there now.

The Arctic charr is an important part of Scotland's biodiversity. In spite of the fact that Scotland has considerable responsibility for the conservation of this fish – it is a stronghold for this species in Europe – Arctic charr have been given little protection in Scotland until recently. Few anglers have previously bothered to fish for charr, but due to the pressures on other species, the Arctic charr is becoming increasingly regarded as an attractive alternative quarry, particularly since the British Record (Rod-caught) Fish Committee has accepted Arctic charr as a trophy fish. It is likely therefore that, in the future, the presence of Arctic charr may be a significant attraction to angling tourists in some parts of Scotland.

Over the last few years also there has been a distinct increase in interest in this species from commercial interests and from fish farmers. It is important that the resource is now looked at closely in relation to these new developments so that there is no danger to the stocks of fish and that any utilisation which takes place is carried out in a sustainable fashion.

Apart from the pressures which have caused extinctions in the past, this valuable fish is now facing a new threat – charr farming. In the last decade of the last century several stocks of Arctic charr were imported from North

America and some of these have been reared in Scottish charr lochs with inevitable escapes and inbreeding with native fish. This means that our charr stocks, isolated for 10,000 years since the last Ice Age, during which each stock has developed its own genetic integrity, are now faced, not only with the usual threats from fish farming (disease, parasites, over-enrichment of lochs) but also with the loss of their unique gene pools. The recent studies by Adams and Huntingford (2004) and others have clearly shown that there there are intriguing differences between different populations of Arctic charr in Scottish lochs (Loch Rannoch has three distinct races) and that this is indeed a species which is undergoing evolution on our own doorstep.

Adams *et al.* (2007) have emphasised that 'the population (rather than the species) makes a more rational unit for the consideration of conservation strategies and that ... management needs may differ significantly between populations.' Though some stocks have been lost in the past, several lochs in the Forth catchment area have retained their populations of Arctic charr and these are an important resource for the future in both scientific and economic terms. Special attention should be given to Lochs Doine, Voil and Lubnaig, which are already part of the River Teith Special Area of Conservation (for lampreys), in order to prevent engineering works and, in particular, the introduction of pike. It is likely that, if Loch Lubnaig had been chosen originally as a water supply for Glasgow (Rankine and Thompson, 1852), its Arctic charr would now be extinct.

Arctic charr: Loch Einich – mature male above, juvenile below.

Acknowledgements

I thank Neville Dix for his helpful editing of the text of this paper. I am grateful also to Colin Bull for data from the Trossachs lochs. Colin Adams was good enough to discuss the value of historical research with me. Acknowledgement is made also to the valuable research files of the late R.P. Hardie and G.F. Friend which are held by the author.

References

Adams, C.E., Fraser, D., Wilson, A.J., Alexander, G., Ferguson, M.M. and Skulason, S. 2007. Patterns of phenotypic and genetic variability show hidden diversity in Scottish Arctic charr. *Ecology of Freshwater Fish*, **16**, 78–86.

Adams, C.E. and Huntingford, F.A. 2004. Incipient speciation driven by phenotypic plasticity? Evidence from sympatric populations of Arctic charr. *Biological Journal of the Linnaean Society*, **81**, 611-618.

Alexander, G. and Adams, C.E. 1999. The Arctic charr in Scotland and Ireland: preliminary results of the first systematic surveys. *Proceedings of the Ninth ISACF Workshop on Arctic charr, Kamchatka.* **1998**, 87-92.

Alexander, G. and Adams, C.E. 2000. Phenotypic variation in Arctic charr from Scotland and Ireland. *Aqua*, **4**, 77-88.

Anonymous. 1843a. Parish of the Port of Menteith, Perth. *New Statistical Account of Scotland*, **10**, 1095-1109.

Anonymous. 1843b. *Perthshire Advertiser*, 20 April, 1843.

Barbour, S. 1984. Variation in Life History, Ecology and Resource Utilisation by Arctic charr *Salvelinus alpinus* (L.) in Scotland. *PhD Thesis, University of Edinburgh.*

Buchanan, G. 1839. Parish of Kinross, Kinross. *New Statistical Account of Scotland*, **9**, 1-29.

Burns-Begg, R. 1874. *The Lochleven Angler*. Kinross: Barnet.

Child, A.R. 1977. Biochemical polymorphism in charr (*Salvelinus alpinus* L.) from Llynnau Peris, Padarn, Cwellyn and Bodlyn. *Heredity*, **38**, 359-365.

Day, F. 1887. *British and Irish Salmonidae*. London: Williams and Norgate.

Ferguson, A. 1981. Systematics of Irish charr as indicated by electrophoretic analysis of tissue proteins. *Biochemical Systematics and Ecology*, **9**, 225-232.

Forbes, A.R. 1905. *Gaelic Names of Beasts (Mammalia), Birds, Fishes, Insects, Reptiles, etc.* Edinburgh: Oliver and Boyd.

Fraser, D., Adams, C.E. and Huntingford, F.A. 1998. Trophic polymorphism among Arctic charr *Salvelinus alpinus* L., from Loch Ericht, Scotland. *Ecology of Freshwater Fish*, **7**, 184-191.

Gordon, J. 1845. *The New Statistical Account of Scotland*. Edinburgh: Blackwood.

Graham, P. 1793. Parish of Aberfoyle, Perth. *Statistical Account of Scotland*, **10**, 113-130.

Graham, R.C. 1843. Parish of Aberfoyle, Perth. *New Statistical Account of Scotland*, **10**, 1150-1160.

Groome, F.M. 1882. *Ordnance Gazetteer of Scotland: a Survey of Scottish Topography, Statistical, Biographical and Historical*. Edinburgh: Jack.

Gunther, A. 1865. Contribution to the knowledge of British charrs. *Annales and Magazine of Natural History*, **12**, 229-239.

Hardie, R.P. 1940. *Ferox and Char in the Lochs of Scotland*. Edinburgh: Oliver and Boyd.

Harriman, R. and Morrison, B.R.S. 1982. The ecology of streams draining forested and non-forested catchments in an area of central Scotland subject to acid precipitation. *Hydrobiologia*, **88**, 251-263.

Hartley, S.E., Bartlett, S.E. and Davidson, W.S. 1992. Mitochondrial DNA analysis of Scottish populations of Arctic charr, *Salvelinus alpinus* (L.). *Journal of Fish Biology*, **40**, 219-224.

Harvie-Brown, J.A. and Buckley, T.E. 1887. *A Vertebrate Fauna of Sutherland, Caithness and West Cromarty*. Edinburgh: Douglas.

Kottelat, M. and Freyhof, J. 2007. *Handbook of European Freshwater Fishes*. Cornol: Kottelat.

Lowther, C. 1629. *Our Journall into Scotland*. Edinburgh: Douglas.

MacFarlane, W. 1723/24. In: *Geographical Collections Relating to Scotland Made by Walter Macfarlane*, Mitchell, A. and Clark, J.T. ed. from Macfarlane's transcript in the Advocate's Library. 3 Vols (Scottish History Society, 1st ser., 51-53). Edinburgh, 1906-8.

Maitland, P.S. 1977. Freshwater fish in Scotland in the 18th, 19th and 20th centuries. *Biological Conservation*, **12**, 265-278.

Maitland, P.S. 1983. The Arctic charr in Scotland. *Proceedings of the Second ISACF Workshop on Arctic charr, Iceland, 1982*, 102-106.

Maitland, P.S., Greer, R.B., Campbell, R.N. and Friend, G.F. 1984. The status and biology of Arctic charr, *Salvelinus alpinus* (L.), in Scotland. In: Johnson, L. and Burns, B. *Biology of the Arctic charr*. pp.193-215. Winnipeg: University of Manitoba.

Maitland, P.S. 1992. The status of Arctic charr, *Salvelinus alpinus* (L.), in southern Scotland: a cause for concern. *Freshwater Forum*, **2**, 212-227.

Maitland, P.S. 1995. World status and conservation of the Arctic charr *Salvelinus alpinus* (L.). *Nordic Journal of Freshwater Research*, **71**, 113-127.

Malloch, P.D. 1910. *Life History of the Salmon, Sea Trout and other Freshwater Fish*. London: Black.

Maxwell, H. 1919. *Memories of the Months, Sixth Series*. London: Arnold.

McGregor, M. 1837. Parish of Balquhidder, Perth. *New Statistical Account of Scotland*, **10**, 344-348.

Morton, W.M. 1955. Charr or Char – history of a common name for *Salvelinus*. *Science*, **121**, 874-875.

Munro, W.R. 1957. The pike of Loch Choin. *Freshwater and Salmon Fisheries Research, Scotland*, **16**, 1-16.

Murray, J. and Pullar, L. 1910. *Bathymetrical Survey of the Freshwater Lochs of Scotland*. Edinburgh: Challenger Office.

Pennant, T. 1769. *A Tour in Scotland*. Chester: Monk.

Rankine, W.M. and Thomson, J. 1852. Comparison of the advantages of Loch Lubnaig and Loch Katrine as sources of water-supply for Glasgow. *Unpublished Report: MS Gen 1675/5*, 59 St Vincent Street, Glasgow.

Regan, C.T. 1911. *The Freshwater Fishes of the British Isles*. London: Methuen.

Regan, C.T. 1914. Systematic arrangement of the fishes of the family Salmonidae. *Annales and Magazine of Natural History*, **13**, 405-408.

Robertson, J. 1794. Parish of Callander, Perth. *Statistical Account of Scotland*, **11**, 574-627.

Robertson, P. 1837. Parish of Callander, Perth. *New Statistical Account of Scotland*, **10**, 349-360.

Sibbald, R. 1710. *The History, Ancient and Modern, of the Sheriffdoms of Fife and Kinross*. Edinburgh: Watson.

Sinclair, J. 1791. *The Statistical Account of Scotland*. Edinburgh: Creech.

Smith, A. 1793. Parish of Kinross, Kinross. *Statistical Account of Scotland*, **6**, 164-173.

Stewart, D. 1793. Parish of Balquhidder, Perth. *Statistical Account of Scotland*, **6**, 88-97.

Stirling, W. 1792. Parish of Port of Monteith, Perth. *Statistical Account of Scotland*, **7**, 139-141.

Stoddart, T.T. 1847. *The Angler's Companion to the Rivers and Lochs of Scotland*. Edinburgh: Blackwood.

LANDSLIDES OF KIPPENRAIT GLEN

Michael F. Thomas

Introduction – Landslides in Scotland

It has long been known that ancient landslides punctuate the slopes of Scotland's hills and mountains. Many of these are rockfalls along cliffs of bare rock, left hanging above the valleys with the retreat of the glaciers more than 11,000 years ago. Others are slides, usually found where the geological strata at depth exhibit weakness and fail, bringing down large masses of overlying rock. The huge landslides at Quirang on the Island of Skye are of this type (Ballantyne, et al., 1998). Most of these falls and slides were active thousands of years ago and pose little threat today, but many slopes remain potentially unstable and shallow slides or flows of loose debris can be induced by adverse weather conditions (often combinations of heavy rainfall and melting snow). These 'debris flows' often occur within existing stream channels, overwhelming the banks, culverts and sometimes bridges with destructive force. Others can start on steep slopes, where seepages occur and flow without following a stream course. All these flows require loose debris to be available on and beneath the hillslope (for a recent general survey see Ballantyne, 2008).

Awareness of the threat from debris flows was raised dramatically by the events in Glen Ogle on 18th August, 2004, when the road was overwhelmed at two locations, trapping 20 vehicles and leading to the rescue of 57 people by helicopter. The heavy rainstorm that triggered these flows was a rare, but probably not unprecedented event: 85 mm of rain fell and 48 mm of that rain occurred in just 20 minutes, reaching a peak intensity of 147 mm/hour (Winter et al., 2005, 2008). It was, however, the exposure to danger of a significant number of people, and the publicity surrounding the rescue that gave urgency to a major review of highway safety in Scotland following this event. An in-depth study was undertaken in cooperation with the Transport Research Laboratory and their first report was published on line in 2005 (Winter et al., 2005), followed in 2008 by a more detailed, Implementation Report (Winter et al., 2008), and a nationwide seminar was held in Glasgow in 2009. The Glen Ogle debris flows were not isolated, and other flows took place over an area of tens of km². A flood in the Keltie Water, destroyed the footbridge at Bracklyn Falls near Callander. Previous destructive flows in the Stirling area have been few, but the risk was made evident in 1984, when an extreme rainfall event led to several slope failures along the Ochil Hills escarpment above Menstrie as a result of a November storm, which had an estimated 50 year recurrence interval (Jenkins et al, 1988). One flow overwhelmed a farmhouse above Menstrie.

Land instability in Kippenrait Glen has been of a different kind, but in February 1999 three small but quite spectacular slides disrupted Glen Road, which had previously been closed, between Bridge of Allan and Dunblane

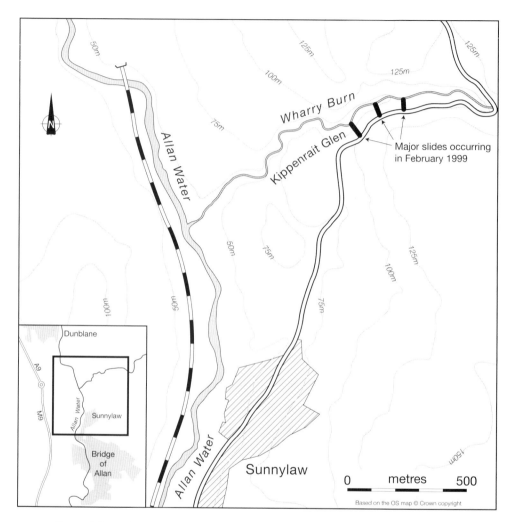

Figure 1. Map showing the location of the three main slides in Kippenrait Glen (inset shows the wider setting north of Bridge of Allan, near Stirling).

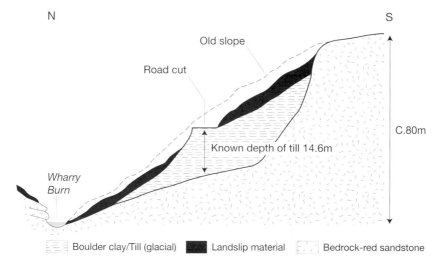

Figure 2. Schematic cross-section (not to scale) showing the relief and geologic setting of the Glen Road in Kippenrait Glen. Bluffs of bedrock outcrop mainly close to the stream channel and can be seen at the site of the bridge. It is thought that the glacial till has filled an older, wider valley.

(Figures 1, 2). These were not debris flows but were slide failures originating below the road pavement. The displaced material from the largest slide developed into an earthflow, which reached the stream channel at the foot of the slope of (Figures 3, 4, 5). The setting and the reasons for these landslides are subjects of this article.

Kippenrait Glen – The Natural Setting

Kippenrait Glen is the name given to the valley of the Wharry Burn, where it flows east to west to join the Allan Water, which in turn flows south into the River Forth near Stirling. The underlying rocks here are the Devonian Old Red Sandstones that extend westward towards the Highland Boundary Fault near Callander, where upturned beds of conglomerate form resistant bands that support the Mentieth Hills. Eastward volcanic, andesite lavas and tuffs increasingly dominate the Devonian sequence, supporting the bold relief of Dumyat Hill and the massif of the Ochils. In the vicinity of Kippenrait Glen and Dunblane, the sandstones are relatively less resistant and form rolling topography. Two outcrops of olivine basalt inter-bedded with the sandstones, however, cross the valley in its upper reaches, one at the site of the road bridge. The Wharry Burn has incised these rocks to form a gorge, but only near the bridge, is fresh rock widely found. Even within the steep ravine, ledges of rock are found mainly bordering the river itself, and the middle and upper slopes are clothed with woodland underlain by poorly drained and often muddy materials, debris left behind by the ice sheet from the last ice age (Figure 2).

This debris is known generically as *till* and much of it is a mixture of boulders, pebbles, sand and boulder clay. The actual clay content of this material is very variable but it is often sufficient to impede drainage and maintain a high moisture content in the surface soils. Its age is uncertain, but it is likely to date from the last glaciation (less than 80,000 years old) and was probably left behind in the valley during the final melting of the local ice (around 15,000 years ago). In geological terms, therefore, these sediments are very young and remain unconsolidated. The way in which the boulder-clay lies in the bedrock valley (Figure 2), to a depth of 14.6 m in a mid-slope position, suggests that there was a more open valley here before glaciation, and it is probable that the final deepening of the valley to form the gorge section was accomplished by both meltwater during de-glaciation and by river erosion during the post-glacial period or Holocene. The boulder-clay is, therefore draped over the older relief and perched above the present river channel. During the phase of down-cutting steep slopes were formed in the till, which have subsequently experienced repeated down-slope movement by sliding and flowage. There is, therefore, a long history of land instability in Kippenrait Glen. Slope values exceed 35° within the inner gorge, and in many places it is too dangerous gain access. Studies world-wide show that slopes between around 27° and 35-40° are most likely to fail. At lower inclinations they become increasingly stable, while very little loose material can survive on much steeper slopes and these become rock outcrops (crags, cliffs).

The woodlands in the glen are recognized as a Site of Special Scientific Interest (SSSI), and they have been studied in some detail (Booth, 2004). The National Vegetation Classification (NVC), based on a ground survey undertaken in 2002, shows two major communities: Old sessile oak woods with holly and hard fern (*Blechnum spicant*) (NVC, W11a) are found mainly on the upper slopes, while Tilio-acerion forests, of slopes, screes and ravines, clothe the inner slopes of the ravine (NVC, W9a). These are characterized by ash, *Fraxinus excelsior*, wych elm *Ulmus glabra* and lime (mainly small-leaved lime *Tilia cordata* but more rarely large-leaved lime *T. platyphyllos*). Introduced sycamore *Acer pseudoplatanus* is often present. The woodland has a high diversity of ground flora and is of ancient origin, remaining largely undisturbed by land use or management and is a Special Area of Conservation (SAC) (see JNCC website).

History of the Glen Road

According to Barty (1944) the upper part of Glen Road including the bridge was built in the 1820s by John Stirling of Kippendavie, who acquired land for the building of the bridge from Lord Abercrombie. Initially a gated, private road, it was made open to the public after insistence that there had, "long been a drove road with a ford near the site of the bridge". While the immediate site of the bridge would have been an unlikely place for a crossing of the Wharry Burn, an old drove road is known to follow a line from Pendreich across Sheriffmuir, crossing the burn at Lynn's Ford, which is shown on Ordnance Survey maps from the 1920s but not on recent editions of the 1:50,000 map series. Since Barty also refers to a route between Bridge of Allan and Dunblane across Sheriffmuir, it seems likely these are one and the same, and the boggy nature of a route across Sheriffmuir was probably a motive for replacing this road. The Darn Road, which passes to the west of Kippenrait Glen is also considered to be an ancient drove road, but offers a more difficult route.

In building the new road it is clear that the pavement was cut into both old slippage debris and the underlying boulder clay, but it is not known if any account was taken of likely problems from landslides. Given the early 19th century date, and the mainly local importance of the road there was probably little thought given to this issue. The natural drainage of the slope was altered, and runoff was channeled into culverts beneath the road. Although some loading of the underlying material subsequently occurred the road was never suitable for heavy traffic. It is clear that in more recent times encroachment of slide material from above has been resisted by installing gabions (wire-netted boulder cages that allow water to infiltrate but retain the slope debris). There are also foundered fence posts downslope from the road, indicating loss of ground from the margins of the road long before the recent landslides took place.

It is also evident that other measures were taken to drain water away from the upper slopes, by digging the trench that runs across the slope and diagonally to join Glen Road, where it approaches the edge of the gorge from the south. There is very little sign that this was, or is, effective in diverting significant runoff. On the other hand, there is evidence that agricultural drains from the fields above the gorge, were built to drain towards the glen, increasing the amount water reaching the road. But in some places these feed into small streams that drain water away from the slope and where these occur the slope appears more stable.

The road was closed by Stirling Council in 1987, due to anxiety about a small slide that had occurred previously and the cost of executing repairs to the bridge. A visual survey by the writer for the community council revealed cambering and cracking of the road pavement in places, as well as fence displacement and minor encroachment of debris from above. It was also clear that the slopes on both sides of the glen had been subject to landslides in the past and that the instability was continuing. At best continued high-cost maintenance of the road would be required with risks of more serious slope failures occurring.

Landslides in Kippenrait Glen

Slope instability has probably been endemic for thousands of years. Before the last major glacial advance around 80,000 years ago, the Wharry Burn was probably a more open valley. As the ice advanced from the highlands, and also built up over the lower ground in the Forth Valley, Kippenrait Glen would have filled with ice. A well-defined glacier occupied the Forth Valley during periods of ice advance and retreat, but the whole area was covered by an ice cap when the glaciation was at its maximum, and it is unlikely that the valley of the

Figure 3. Head scar of the largest landslide photographed in April 1999: 2-3 m of substratum and nearly half the original road width was lost in this event.

Figure 4. View from the toe of the main landslide in April 1999, showing the debris flow. Trees fell backwards (upslope) as their roots were carried down-slope. The toe of the main landslide intersected the channel of the Wharry Burn, but the height and volume of material was insufficient to cause a lake to form (photo April, 1999).

Figure 5. Toe of the main slide in April 1999. The earth/debris flow reached the stream channel at the base of the hillslope but failed to block the flow of water.

Figure 6. Slope failure above the roadway, near the crest of the slope, is unrelated to the existence of the road. Many such failures can be seen on both sides of the Glen, and they reflect the wider slope instability in Kippenrait Glen (photo march 2006).

Figure 7. Debris flow leading from an upslope landslide and forming part of the slope above the roadway (photo March 2006).

Figure 8. State of the head scar of the main landslide in April 2009. Patchy re-vegetation can be seen but, in places the slide has been re-activated leading to small-scale slides and flows.

Figure 9. Detail from the middle slide in April, 2009. This shows widening of the slide as well as headward recession with renewed flows down-slope (net changes are probably around 0.5 m in each event).

Figure 10. View of the scar taken from across the valley. This shows how blocks of unconsolidated till rapidly break up into debris flows on the steep slopes below the road (slopes exceed 35° in many places).

Wharry Burn ever contained a true glacier. But as highland ice moved across the area it deposited debris as boulder clay, plugging the old valleys.

During the glacial maxima sea levels were lowered, by more than 100 m, and remained low during de-glaciation, when meltwater, including sub-glacial streams, would have eroded the valleys draining the Ochils and other hill masses, to create steep gullies and gorges, including that of the Wharry Burn. This erosion would have removed much of the till from the centre of the valley, leaving an uneven spread of boulder clay along the valley sides. Early in the Holocene sea levels recovered rapidly leading to the deposition of more than 20 m of estuarine sediment in the Forth Valley, but this would not have affected the streams draining adjacent hills.

At first, the withdrawal of the ice would have left steepened slopes unsupported in a cold climate with harsh winter conditions of frost and snow, followed by spring melting. There may also have been earth tremors as a result of the unloading of ice from the Scottish mainland. Rockfalls were common, and can be seen in Glen Ogle, and also along the escarpments of the Gargunnock and Campsie Hills, where a sequence of sedimentary rocks is capped by basaltic lava, and failure took place along bedding planes above waterlogged, impermeable shales. Some of these were deep-seated, rotational slides, where the failure plane describes a semi-circular shape. At Lees Hill along the Gargunnock escarpment it is still possible to stand on the lip of one such rotated block, the land sloping inward towards the cliff above. It is also possible to see how a major rockfall has later filled part of the void left by the slide.

Such processes were widespread across Scotland and Ballantine (2002, 2008) has described them as *paraglacial* adjustments, and the process continues. Events in Kippenrait Glen are on a smaller scale. The Devonian sandstones are relatively stable, and there is no cap-rock to produce a cliff below the summit. The major susceptibilities here are the junction between the boulder clay and the sandstone bedrock (Figure 2), and a tendency for the till to become waterlogged and subject to superficial flows and failures, some 1-3 metres deep. These can be seen just below the crest of the slope on both sides of the valley and they often take the form of slides, which have left small cuspate scars (Figure 6). At lower levels, particularly on the (colder, wetter) north-facing slope followed by the road, most of these slides have disintegrated into flows of mud and stones (Figure 7). Many of these have travelled only a few metres and tend to encroach on to the road from above only occasionally, as bulges which can be trimmed back. In the upper part of the glen the cut slope has been supported with gabions. The way in which these slides and flows operate can be seen in the displacement of trees and fence posts. While some trees loose support and topple forwards, many others are rotated backward by the slides and their root mats become exposed and face down-slope. The gradual and episodic nature of these movements is also demonstrated by trees that recover after slide events and develop new or curved trunks.

Why then did three quite large slides take place suddenly in the later winter of 1999? This was 12 years after closure to traffic in 1987. The slides broke away close to the edge of the road pavement, in one case taking a significant amount of the tarmac with it (Figure 3). The displaced blocks would have broken up as they collapsed to form earth flows towards the base of the slopes, intersecting the stream channel, but not completely blocking it (Figure 5). It is not known if all three occurred on the same day. These events led to new fencing, road barriers and landslide warnings. Several minor events have since taken place to enlarge the original scars, and some of the first new fences have had to be replaced (Figures 8, 9). The Glen Road currently remains as a footpath and cycle track.

Clearly the existence of the road must have been a major factor, since all three slides fell away close to the edge of the pavement, whereas the majority of other slides have no direct connection to the road or its construction. The road had been in existence for more than 150 years without catastrophic failure and, therefore, it is evident that some particular explanation is required for these events. Candidates must be either change to the environmental conditions or to the condition of the road itself.

There is widespread evidence from Scotland and the rest of northern Europe for important climate fluctuations during the Holocene on decadal to centennial timescales and these were related to periods of greater activity in slope instability and flooding, with intervals of quiescence (see Reid and Thomas, 2006). There were many such episodes, including the enigmatic Little Ice Age, which in reality was a series of 'cold' events spaced over several centuries, spanning the great famine of the 14th Century and the icy winters of the second half of the 17th Century, immortalised by Flemish and other artists of the period. But there is no recorded evidence for these events in Kippenrait Glen. Another factor that operates to destabilise hillslopes is the unnoticed, gradual downslope movement of material that may accumulate in hollows perched above the valley floor. When such accumulations thicken their water-holding capacity increases, and this can lead to failure and flowage after prolonged, wet periods. Exceptionally wet conditions also occur annually in an unpredictable way: either in terms of higher monthly or seasonal averages or as extreme events (storms). The debris flows in Glen Ogle and elsewhere on 18th August 2004 were triggered by an intense rainstorm lasting only a few hours. But other types of landslide are less likely to be the results extreme events. They are more likely to respond to prolonged periods of exceptionally wet conditions. Studies of such antecedent rainfalls have not established any general relationships and the question of how far back in time rainfall records should be analysed is unclear. The relevant period could be a few days, weeks or months, perhaps even longer.

Finally, the modification of slopes and, particularly slope drainage by engineering work, frequently compounds the natural factors favouring instability. The undercutting of slopes removes support for deposits above the cut, and such slopes are usually protected by gabions, concrete or other barriers. Undercutting also occurs naturally by stream erosion on outer bends of channels and this often leads to slides from the lower slopes of valleys. The loading and sealing of unconsolidated sediments such as till or other clay materials by engineering structures can be a complicating factor affecting free drainage, and it is to these that we should look first in the case of the 1999 slides at Kippenrait Glen.

When the Glen Road was closed by Stirling Council in 1987, maintenance of the bridge continued but the road was abandoned to natural processes. Dominant amongst these was encroachment of sediment from above: either brought down by small streams or by the formation of bulges by the slow creep of bulk material. This sediment was mixed with organic debris from the slope and quickly nourished the growth of small plants, which further reduced the transport of sediment away from the road. Ponding of surface water and retention of moisture within the sediments below the road as a consequence of prolonged slow seepage along the back of the tarmac occurred and was almost certainly responsible for the landslides that took place in 1999. It is difficult to pinpoint exactly why it should have taken this precise period of time to fail. But the Autumn of 1998 was exceptionally wet and 171 % of 30 year average rainfall fell in October, after a cool and wet summer. In January 1999 rainfall was also nearly 24 % above average and the Allan Water flooded on the 14th and 18th. Although February was drier with only 90 % of average rainfall, 19 mm of rain fell on the 27th and the Allan Water flooded again on 28th February (see Harrison, 1998, 1999). All these factors appear to have contributed to the slope failures, which took place shortly after this event (this interpretation was advanced by Thomas, 2002 in a Symposium lecture to FNH, and is also found in Booth, 2004). The location of all three slides partly reflects the slightly concave plan of the slope at all three points. Concavities concentrate water both above and below ground contributing to greater wetness through time.

One further factor of some importance is the *aspect* of the slopes. The road follows the southern flank of the valley, and the slopes affected by the landslides all face N or NNW. This means that they only receive direct sunlight in the late afternoon or evening, and never during the winter months. Slopes on the opposing slope face S or SSE and receive significantly more sunlight and can be expected to dry out more often. But they are not free from slope failures. On the contrary, there are several places where quite large slides have taken place and these can be seen from the path that runs along the crest of the slope. But in most cases the slides appear to have remained intact and they have become vegetated. They form elongate, bench-like features below the upper slopes. There are, however, few signs of the repeated shallow failures and flows of material that afflict the whole of the wetter, north-facing slope. This contrast has contributed to the overall steepness of the south-facing slope which, although too dangerous to conduct many ground readings, is thought to maintain the steepest slopes in the valley. This is logical, since the north-facing valley-side is losing material from the upper slopes by repeated small ruptures and earthflows.

Details of the Landslides and Subsequent Events

All three, recent slides are characterised by a clean break in the road pavement at the head of the slide. Below this a steep, near vertical, erosional scar was left exposed as the slide material moved rapidly downslope, breaking up into a flow of mud and boulders (Figure 10). The toe of the largest slide invaded the valley floor and reached the stream, but was not sufficient to cause a prolonged blockage (Figures 1-4). Each slide is a discrete entity and they are not adjoining. Technically these are translational slides and each scar face approximates to upper part of a plane of shear failure. The roadway was cut into the boulder clay (Figure 2), and this tends to be more compacted than the overlying hill-slope debris, which explains why these failures are slides and appear different from the many minor slips and flows elsewhere in the valley.

Since their formation in 1999, the slides have been revisited in most years and photographs taken at intervals (in early April before becoming obscured by foliage). Small incremental changes have occurred and the fencing erected by Stirling Council has needed renewal more than once as the pavement has given way (Figures 7, 8, 9). But the formation of scars has had the effect of improving the drainage of the till, which is now probably less likely to experience deep failure at these locations. The slides are now mainly affected by surface flows of water and by frost damage to the tarmac edges. No new slides have directly affected the road, but in several places material buttressing the slope below the road level is sliding downs-lope, and further rapid movements cannot be ruled out. So long as runoff from the road feeds into the existing slides they are also likely to remain fresh in appearance, seasonal plant growth being disrupted in most years (Figure 8). These active hillslope processes also contribute to local biodiversity, by opening up the woodland canopy, and by diversifying edaphic conditions. It has been established elsewhere that geomorphological heterogeneity contributes to biodiversity in a variety of settings (Burnett et al., 1998).

Summary and Conclusions

Kippenrait Glen is effectively a river gorge that has been deepened by the present Wharry Burn since the end of the last ice age. The river is cutting into an older valley that was previously filled with ice, which left a cover of boulder clay. The steep slopes have proved unstable in the humid climates that have prevailed for much of the Holocene, and they are pock-marked by shallow slides and, in the case of the north-facing slope covered by small earth and mud flows. The imposition of the road adversely affected the hydrology of the north-facing slope, and left upper slopes undercut in places. Road maintenance, particularly of culverts and drains, avoided catastrophic failure for around 150 years. But the existence of artificial drains, gabions and displaced fencing demonstrates the repeated efforts to maintain this road against slope instability.

Eventually, in the late 1980s concerns had grown about the future of the road and three boreholes were drilled near the slide close to the bridge. These proved the depth of till in the old valley (14.6 m) and the predicted cost of maintaining the road as a safe passage for motorists led to closure in 1987. The lack of road maintenance in the ensuing decade contributed to the slope instability, with three slides being opened up during the winter of 1999. Thus although these slides are in part a consequence of road building and lack of maintenance, they are set within a valley that has experienced repeated slope instability for thousands of years. The vegetation cover reflects this state of affairs, with many bent and fallen trees: some uprooted; others dying due to disruption of their root systems. There will be ongoing slides and flows in this valley and eventually the road will be consumed, but not perhaps for some decades.

References

Ballantyne, C.K., 2002. A general model of paraglacial landscape response. *The Holocene* 12, 371-376.

Ballantyne, C.K., 2008. Landslides and slope failures in Scotland: a review. *Scottish Geographical Magazine* 102, 134-150.

Ballantyne C.K., Stone J.O., Fifield L.K., 1998. Cosmogenic Cl-36 dating of postglacial landsliding at the Storr, Isle of Skye, Scotland. *Holocene.* 8, 347-351.

Ballantyne C.K., Benn D.I., Lowe J.J., and Walker M.J.C. 1991. *The Quaternary of the Isle of Skye: Field Guide*, Cambridge: Quaternary Research Association.

Barty, A., 1944. *The History of Dunblane.* Stirling: Eneas McKay.

Booth, A. (2004). NVC survey of Kippenrait Glen SSSI/cSAC. Scottish Natural Heritage, Commissioned Report No. 046 (ROAME No. F02LG14).

Burnett, M.R., August P.V., Brown Jr. J.H. and Killingbeck K.T., 1998. The influence of geomorphological heterogeneity on biodiversity: I. A patch-scale perspective Source: *Conservation Biology* v12 n2: 363-370.

Harrison, S.J. (ed.), 1998, 1999. *Annual Climatological Bulletin,* Numbers: 20 (1998), 21 (1999). University of Stirling, Department of Environmental Science.

Jenkins, A., Ashworth, R., Ferguson, R.I., Grieve, I.C., Rowling, P, and Stott, T.A., (1988). Slope failures in the Ochil Hills, Scotland November 1984. *Earth Surface Processes and Landforms* 13, 69-76.

Joint Nature Conservation Committee (JNCC). Special Areas of Conservation (SACs) , Sites in Scotland – Kippenrait Glen. See www.jncc.gov.uk/protectedsites/

OS Popular Edition, 1:63,360 Map, dating to 1920-30, available on-line from National Library of Scotland. See www.nls.uk/

Reid, E. and Thomas, M.F., 2006. A chronostratigraphy of mid and late-Holocene slope evolution: Creagan a' Chaorainn, Northern Highlands of Scotland. *The Holocene* 16, 429-444.

Winter, M.G., Macgregor, F., and Shackman, L., 2005. Scottish Road Network Landslides Study, 2005. Section 9 Summary. The Scottish Government publications. Available on-line at http://www.scotland.gov.uk/Publications/2005/07/08131738/17395.

Winter, M.G., Macgregor, F., and Shackman, L., 2008. publications, (2008). Scottish Road Network Landslides Study, Implementation. The Scottish Government publications. Available on line at http://www.transportscotland.gov.uk/reports/publications-and-guidance/road/j10107-00.htm).

FORTH AREA BIRD REPORT 2008

A.E. Thiel and C.J. Pendlebury

This report is the 34th bird report for the Forth Valley (or Upper Forth) bird recording area. The area covered by the report comprises the council areas of Falkirk, Clackmannan and Stirling, excluding Loch Lomondside and other parts of the Clyde drainage basin. Please note that we do not include the Endrick Water, i.e. Fintry and Balfron.

The report was written by Chris Pendlebury (non-passerines, excluding waders) and Andre Thiel (waders, passerines and escapees) with Cliff Henty contributing the half-monthly summaries to the wader accounts. Chris Pendlebury, as SOC recorder can be contacted by e-mail at chris@upperforthbirds.co.uk, by leaving a message on 07798 711134 or by mail to 3 Sinclair Street, Dunblane FK15 0AH.

The main part of the report consists of detailed species accounts presented in a systematic list now arranged in the new order, as adopted by the BOU, and using the new nomenclature, as recommended by the SOC. This is preceded by a summary of the main bird news from the past year and a Ringing Report, both compiled by Andre Thiel.

ROUND-UP OF THE YEAR

January

January started with a Spotted Redshank at Kinneil on 1st. On 2nd the overwintering Spotted Sandpiper that had been present since 24th December 2007 made its first appearance in the new year. As it drew the crowds to Kinneil, at nearby Polmonthill a Firecrest – another first for the recording area – was an excellent find on 3rd. It remained rather elusive during its stay until 26th. As in the two preceding years, a Ruff overwintered at Skinflats where it was seen on 4th. On 5th an overwintering Common Greenshank was on the River Avon at Grangemouth and the next day two birds were at Skinflats and one at Kinneil. The first Barnacle Goose of the year was seen at Skinflats on 11th. The next day was pretty productive. The first evidence of overwintering Green Sandpipers came with two birds on the River Carron. The drake Green-winged Teal that had been present at Kinneil since 21st December 2007 was spotted again there. Fifty Common Snipe on the Forth along the Stirling-Upper Taylorton stretch was a good count, while the first two Bramblings of the year were at Longleys, Carse of Lecropt with further singles in Dunblane on 20th and Blairdrummond Moss on 22nd. A small remnant flock of Bohemian Waxings from 2007 remained in Dunblane where 24 birds were seen on 15th. An immature White-tailed Eagle from the Fife reintroduction scheme at Argaty, Braes of Doune on 23rd was the first of a run of sightings in our area.

February

A mini influx of Snow Buntings saw five birds at Craigmore in Aberfoyle on

2nd, two birds at the Duke's Pass, Aberfoyle on 3rd and 2 birds at Earlsburn on 9th. An overwintering Green Sandpiper was on Loch Daira at Blairdrummond on 3rd as were two Bramblings at Bows, Braes of Doune. Another Green Sandpiper was at Gilston Park in Polmont on 7th. A Eurasian Woodcock taking its time to cross a road near Dollarbeg on 7th was an amusing sight. A Rock Pipit at Tullibody Inch on 9th was the only one of the year. Presumably the same adult Ring-billed Gull as in 2007 was again seen at Kinneil on 9th, 10th, 11th, 16th and 17th. Seventy Northern Pintail at Skinflats on 10th was the largest flock of the year. Also on 10th an adult Mediterranean Gull at Kinneil was the 13th record for the area and started a run of four more sightings of a species that is spreading. A count of 60 Willow Ptarmigan (Red Grouse) at Cringate Muir also on 10th must have been satisfying. Twenty Common Pochard at Carron Valley Res on 12th was, surprisingly, the largest flock of the year. A Spotted Redshank was at Skinflats on 28th and 29th.

March

Good numbers of Pink-footed Geese were counted in the Forth catchment area with 3000 birds on Thornhill Carse on 9th and 2500 at Lake of Menteith on 27th. A drake Green-winged Teal at Cambusmore on 17th constitutes the 5th record for the recording area, while a drake Lesser Scaup at Vale of Coustry on 19th was the fourth record. Three Red-throated Divers off Kinneil on 29th was the largest count of the year. The advent of spring was heralded by the first Sand Martins of the year in Doune on 30th, albeit rather late. The same day also saw the first Common Chiffchaffs arrive in Falkirk and Doune.

April

Late Redwings left Auchinlay, Dunblane on 4th. The next day 30 Black-legged Kittiwakes passed Kinneil. The first Barn Swallow of the year at Gart gravel pits on 6th was rather late as were the first Northern Wheatears north of Menstrie. The 8th saw the first Willow Warbler at Skinflats. A small spring passage of Common Greenshank started at Kinneil on 12th with a single bird, rising to three individuals by 28th. On 14th the long-staying Spotted Sandpiper was last seen at Kinneil bringing to an end an almost four-month long presence. Two days later a Wood Nuthatch at Blairdrummond caravan park was the 6th record for the recording area, continuing a good run since the first bird was recorded in 1999 and constitutes another piece in the jigsaw of the northwards spread of the species in Scotland. The same day saw the first House Martins arrive in the same location and slightly later than in the past. On 17th and 24th a ringed Black-tailed Godwit of the Icelandic race that had been ringed the previous winter on the Atlantic coast of France was spotted at Kinneil. The first Whimbrel of the year appeared at Skinflats on 18th with two birds there on 26th. The 23rd saw the first Common Grasshopper Warbler at Blairdummond and the first Garden Warbler at Cocksburn, followed by the first Common Whitethroat at Skinflats on 24th and the first Common Cuckoo at Flanders Moss on 25th. Four Hooded Crows at Skinflats on 26th were in a rather unusual location. 27th was a good day for witnessing the spring arrival of migrants with Common Swifts in Bridge of Allan, Tree Pipits at Argaty, Braes of Doune and Dumyat Stirling, a Common Redstart at Menteith and a Sedge Warbler at Skinflats. A poor passage of Green Sandpipers consisted of three birds at Kinneil on 28th. The month finished with the first Wood Warbler of the year at Kippenrait Glen, Bridge of Allan on 30th.

May

Whinchats arrived slightly later than in previous years with the first near Clackmannan on 2nd. A moulting Spotted Redshank on 4th and 5th May at Kinneil had apparently been present there since the start of the year. Two Little Gulls at Skinflats, on the other hand, were definitely the first of the year. The 7th saw the last flock of 74 Pink-footed Geese as well as four Eurasian Wigeon at Alloa Inch. A pair of maybe the same birds was seen at the nearby Blackdevon Wetlands two days later. On 10th a White Stork flew SE past Fallin. A pair of Spotted Flycatchers on 13th at Doune Lodge, Braes of Doune spearheaded a rather poor showing of this declining African migrant. Likewise two Pied Flycatchers at Brig o'Turk on 24th were, surprisingly, the only record of the year. The second Mediterranean Gull of the year was at Blairdrummond on 25th, while a Ring Ouzel on Ben Ledi on 29th was the only one seen this year.

June

A pair of Eurasian Teal at Blackdevon Wetlands on 4th could have been breeding there. On 11th three first-summer Little Gulls were spotted at Skinflats. A showy male Common Rosefinch in Tyndrum on 19th was an excellent find. This is the 5th record for the recording area and continues a run since 1997, prompting thoughts of when rather than whether breeding will occur. Two Eurasian Wigeon and 6 Eurasian Teal at Loch Dochat on 21st fall into the same category of possible breeders. A good autumn passage of Common Greenshank started at Skinflats on 25th with two birds. A flock of 50 Common Crossbills in Hermitage Wood, Bridge of Allan on 28th was a good showing.

July

Two adult Eurasian Spoonbills at Kinneil on 2nd-the 6th record for the recording area – livened up the 'quiet' month with a protracted stay that lasted until the end of August. A Common Quail at Thornhill on 7th and 17th would have enlivened the observer's day. The autumn passage of Common Greenshank at Skinflats gathered speed with seven birds on 7th. The first two Arctic Skuas of the autumn flew past Kinneil on 10th with one there on 23rd. Four Sanderling at Kinneil on 16th was only one of two sightings of the species this year. A Ruddy Turnstone was at Kinneil on 27th and on the same day the third Mediterranean Gull of the year at Skinflats. Whimbrel passage peaked with ten birds at Kinneil on 29th.

August

Two more Ruddy Turnstones were at Kinneil on 1st. A moulting flock of 3259

Common Shelduck was seen in the Grangemouth area on 2nd. A European Shag at Kinneil on the same day as well as on 17th and 24th was a unusual record. Autumn passage of Ruff started on 13th with three birds at Skinflats and quickly increased to eight birds on 19th. The 13th also saw the continuing Common Greenshank passage with five birds at Skinflats increasing to eight on 16th, 11 on 22nd and 25th and 10 on 29th. Also on the same day there was an adult Little Gull at Kinneil that was also seen there on 17th and 23rd. The adult Ring-billed Gull made another appearance at Kinneil on 14th. Green Sandpiper passage was poor with singles at Kinneil and Gilston on 14th, 15th and 28th. Single Whimbrel on 16th and 22nd at Kinneil increased to a second peak of ten birds on 25th. Black-tailed Godwit numbers at Kinneil peaked at 325 on 29th. The first sighting of two juvenile Curlew Sandpipers at Skinflats on 31st was rather late.

September

A Wood Nuthatch on feeders in Bridge of Allan on 5th constitutes the 2nd records of the year and the 7th for the Forth Valley recording area. Five Arctic Skuas and 50 Black-legged Kittiwakes at Kinneil on 6th were good sightings. The Ring-billed Gul made another intermittent stop at Kineil on 6th and 13th. Eight Curlew Sandpipers at Skinflats from 14th to 18th was a good showing. Seventeen adult Little Gulls flying past Kinneil on 17th was an excellent observation. If confirmation that autumn had arrived was needed, it came in the form of four Pale-bellied Brent Geese at Skinflats on 20th increasing to 11 on 21st to 23rd. A juvenile Pectoral Sandpiper at Tullibody Inch on 26th was only the 3rd for the Forth Valley, the first two records beng in May and September 1987, respectively. A single Brent Goose at Kinneil on 28th was probably one of the Skinflats birds.

October

A drake Green-winged Teal moulting out of eclipse plumage at Kinneil on 5th – possibly the same bird that was present there in January – is the earliest recorded in Scotland. Fifteen immature Northern Gannets passing Skinflats on 10th was a good count. Two Snow Buntings were on Ben Ledi on 11th. A Slavonian Grebe at Loch Coulter on 14th was the first of three birds this year with the second at Lake of Menteith on 17th close on its heels. A Red-necked Grebe at Blackness on 18th was the first of two birds this year. A Brambling was in Dunblane on 20th. On 25th a first winter Mediterranean Gull was at Kinneil. On 26th the Whooper Swan flock at Skinflats peaked at a good 65 birds. Two days later saw the only White-fronted Geese of the year make landfall there, consisting of 11 birds of the Greenland race.

November

November started with the first Bohemian Waxwings of an invasion in South Alloa, Fallin and Strathyre on 1st. Single figure arrivals quickly grew to over 200 on 11th and 12th in Stirling, 200 as well in Dunblane on 21st and 220 on

22nd before starting to dwindle again. The first day of the month also saw a Snow Bunting over Blairdrummond with two more birds at Loch Ard on 3rd and 1 at Kinneil on 22nd. Two overwinering Common Greenshank were at Kinneil from 11th, while up to five birds were at Skinflats from 15th. An immature Long-tailed Duck there from 15th to 24th was one of only two this year. Greater Canada Geese continue to thrive with a peak count of 260 at Loch Venachar on 16th. The same day an overwintering Green Sandpiper was on the River Carron between the M876 and Larbert with another one at Quarry Pond, Blairdrummond on 24th. A female Common Scoter at Kinneil on 18th was the only one of the year. The third Slavonian Grebe of the year was seen at Cambusmore on 21st; the fifth Mediterranean Gull at Skinflats on 23rd and the second Red-necked Grebe of the year at Cocksburn Reservoir on 26th. The 25th was the last time the Ring-billed Gull was spotted at Kinneil.

December

A count of 50 Red Kites at Argaty, Braes of Doune on 4th would have been an impressive sight. There were several records of Barnacle Geese this year. A flock of seven birds at Brackenlees Fm, Powfoulis on 7th was the largest one. An adult Iceland Gull at the Avondale landfill site in Polmont was the only record for the year. Another overwintering Green Sandpiper was at Coustry Pond on 18th. The second Long-tailed Duck of the year was at Carron Valley Reservoir on 21st, while the largest count of Greater Scaup was made at Kinneil on 24th with 35 birds. A flock of 80 Common Eider off Kinneil on 26th was another good count. An overwintering Ruff – possibly the same bird as the one that overwintered previously – was seen at Skinflats on the same day. The year ended on 31st with still a sizeable flock of 50 Bohemian Waxwings in Tullibody.

RECORD SUBMISSION AND REPORT FORMAT

Annual Bird Reports depend largely on contributions from the local birdwatching community. Due to the ever growing (and welcome) volume of data that are submitted, some data that may be of relevance in one year may not be so in another year. This should not discourage contributors from submitting data that they feel are of relevance to their local area, as it will only become obvious whether a particular record should be included or not once the entire dataset is available. Several observers send in a list largely or entirely for their home locality. Much of this information is not suitable for inclusion in these annual reports but is valuable to have on record (e.g. for conservation action). These data are kept in a special file. At the moment there are fifteen such lists referring to the whole district from Falkirk to Killin. Several contributors send in data, often of common species, from repeated transect visits to the same locality, e.g. Airthrey; King's Park, Stirling; Cobleland, Aberfoyle. This has become more common since the advent of the BTO's Birdtrack on-line project. Such data reflect birds per walked route rather than flock sizes. These data are especially useful, if collected repeatedly and using the same effort between years, in which case they allow valid comparison between seasons and years to be made.

To facilitate the preparation of the report, contributors are strongly encouraged to submit their data as soon as possible after the end of the year. Electronic files are much the preferred format, as it greatly speeds up cross-checking and summarising of data. A standard spreadsheet is available from Chris Pendlebury. Special thanks are due to those contributors who are submitting their data in this format.

Following appeals for more complete information, most records now include the name of the nearest village and an increasing number of records are also submitted with 6-figure grid references. This is very much appreciated, as it enormously speeds up cross-checks and is a valuable resource for conservation action.

The sparse information available about common breeding species is improved by data from the Breeding Birds Survey (BBS). For less common species data can sometimes be summarised in terms of the numbers of pairs or apparently occupied territories for particular locations. The organisers for both the estuary and the inland waters parts of the national wildfowl counts (WeBS) have also made available the results from these for this report. Where appropriate, these data are included in the species accounts.

For many species the records sent in are very unrepresentative of their general distribution. This applies particularly to very common species or to those that are secretive or breed in inaccessible locations. The status of species is detailed in a check list, published in the *Forth Naturalist and Historian*, Vol 15. In addition there is a coded summary of general distribution after the species name. This often apparently contradicts the detailed records that are published for the year. The codes are thus:

B - Breeding status: widespread (present in more than five 10 km squares)
b   "   "   :   local, scarce (present in fewer than five 10 km squares)
W - Winter status: widespread or often in groups of more than ten
w -   "   "   :   local, scarce (usually fewer than ten in a group)
P or p :   Passage (used when species is usually absent in winter; P or p used for widespread or local as in winter status)
S or s :   Summer visitor (used for species present in summer but which do not normally breed; S or s used for widespread or local as in winter status).

Thus BW would be appropriate for European Robin, B for Barn Swallow, p for Ruff and SW for Great Cormorant. No status letter is used if a species occurs less than every other year.

Vetting of records of species that are unusual locally is carried out by a panel of five members, which currently consists of C. Pendlebury, C. Henty, D. Orr-Ewing, D. Douglas and A. McIver. The panel has produced a list of species that are scarce locally and where the records need to be supported by either a full description or sufficient evidence to remove any reasonable doubt. The list is available from Chris Pendlebury. Any species which is a vagrant to the area and some of those which are asterisked (*) in this report will fall in this category. At the discretion of the panel a description may also be required for more common species. The first twenty occurrences of a species in our recording area are highlighted. Vetting of national rarities is done by the BBRC and that of Scotish rarities by the SBRC; descriptions need to be submitted to these committees, as appropriate.

The British Ornithologists' Union (BOU) has appealed in the past for introduced/escaped species to be recorded locally. As the published information on these species is not necessarily complete, it is important to monitor changes in the status of these species more accurately. The BOU therefore encourages observers to record and monitor all naturalised species (particularly but not exclusively breeding records and interactions with native species) and escaped species seen in the wild to assist it to make future recommendations for category C status, if a self-sustaining naturalised population is established.

The following abbreviations have been used in the report: Ad(s) - adult(s), AoT - apparently occupied territory, b/lkm - birds per linear kilometre, Br - bridge, BoA - Bridge of Allan, BoD - Braes of Doune, ca - circa, c/n - clutch of n eggs, conf. - confluence, BBS - Breeding Bird Survey, CP - Country Park, E - east, Est - estuary, Fm - farm, F - Female, G - Glen, GP - gravel pit, Imm - immature, incl - including, Juv - juvenile, L - Loch, N - north, NR - Nature Reserve, nr - near, M - Male, Max - maximum, ON - on nest; pr - pair; Res - Reservoir, R - river, Rd - road, S - south, SP - summer plumage, W - west, WeBS - Wetland Bird Survey, Y - young, > flying/flew.

CONTRIBUTORS

This report has been compiled from records submitted by the contributors listed below. Where initials are given, the contributors are listed in the species entries of birds which are rare, uncommon or otherwise noteworthy.

B. Allan (BA), D. Anderson (DA), M. Albert (MIA), M. Anderson (MA), S. Ashworth, P. Ashworth (PA), G. Auty, A. Ayre, L Barber, Bean Goose Action Group (BGAG), D. Beaumont (DB), G. Bell (GFB), M. Bell (MVB), N. Bielby (NB), Birdguides (BRG), A. Blair (AB), R.A. Broad (RAB), D.M. Bryant (DMB), A. Burrows (ABu), J. Calladine (JRC), G. Cannon, I. Carmichael, A. Carrington-Cotton (ACC), A. Carroll (AC), V Carroll, P. Carter, S. Chadwick (SC), R. Chapman, D. and A. Christie (DAC), C. Clark, N. Clark, K. Conlin, G. Cook (GC), J. Cowan, R. Cranston, J. Crook (JC), R. Dalziel (RDZ), R. and H. Dawson (RHD), A. Derks, D. Dunion, R. Eaves (RE), D. Eggerton, T. Findlay (TF), J. Fotheringham (JFo), G. Fraser, J. Fulton, E. Gallagher (EG), B. Galpin (BG), G. Garner (GG), T. Goater, D. Goodwin (DG), R. Griffiths, D. Haines (DH), A. Hannah, K. Hemple (KH), I. Henderson, C. Henty (CJH), L. Hesp, E. Hurley (EH), D. Irving (DI), D. Jones, P. Jones, J. Kaye, D. Kerr (DK), G. Kett, R. Knight, A. Lauder (AL), G. and E. Leisk (GEL), P. Lubbers (PAL), B. Lynch, W. MacAlpine (WM), C. Mallett (CJM), C. Marshall, D. Matthews, L. McBrien, M. McDowall, M. McGinty, C. McInerny (CM), D. Merrie, S. Milligan (SM),

C. Moore (CMO), D. Morrison (DM), F. Murray, K. Ogilvie (KO), D. Orr-Ewing (DOE), B. Osborn (BO), G. Owens (GO), E. and J. Payne, C. Pendlebury (CJP), R. Penn (RP), D. Pickett (DP), K. Pilkington, S. Pinder (SP), R. Ridley (RR), W. Rankine (WR), A.C. Rogers (ACR), N. Rossiter (NR), R. and S. Sexton (RSx), R. Shand (RS), J. Shanks, K. Shaw (KDS), G. Skipper (GS), E. Smith, K. Smith (KS), A. Thiel (AET), W. Thom (WT), D. Thorogood (DT), J. Towill (JT), C. Twist (CT), C. Walker, C. Wernham, A. Westwood (AW), G. Wilkinson (GW), K. Wilkinson, A. Williams, G. Wood (GW), M. Wotherspoon (MWO), H. Young (HY).

WeBS estuary counts are made available by M. Bell and N Bielby. Apologies to anybody who has been inadvertently missed out of the above list.

RINGING REPORT

This is the fifth ringing report. The following section lists all ringed birds seen in the recording area during the year. Contributors are encouraged to report colour-ringed wildfowl to the relevant organisers and/or the BTO and not to assume that somebody else has already done so, as all movements are of interest to the ringers and add to our understanding of bird ecology and migration patterns. Thanks are due to Allan and Lyndesay Brown and Kirstie Hemple for making available data on movements of birds seen in the recording area. Allan and Lyndesay Brown, who are ringing Mute Swans in Fife and the Lothians, are particularly keen to learn if any of the birds ringed by them (green or white Darvic rings) breed outside their study area.

Twelve recoveries (excluding multiple sightings of the same bird) were made in 2008. Most are of Mute Swan (11) with one recovery of a Black-tailed Godwit. The total number of species for which ringing recovery information is now available for our area (since 2004) stands at 23 species.

Recoveries are listed in the new order, as for the systematic list, under the headings shown below. Where an asterisk appears behind a ring number, further details of sightings are given in previous ringing reports.

Ring number	Date ringed	Location ringed	Date seen in 2008	Location in recording area (codes as in main list)	Recorder

followed by the location(s) where the bird was seen in between

•MUTE SWAN

Green IVU	13 Aug 2005	Union Canal, Viewforth, Edinburgh	4 Jan 2008	Gartmorn Dam (C)	KH
Green IXZ	14 Aug 2004	Union Canal, Polmont (F)	11 Oct 2008	Forth and Clyde Canal, Bankside (F)	KH

In care Middlebank 20 Oct 2005 to 4 Dec 2005. Released Linlithgow Loch 4 Dec 2005. Seen there 27 Aug 2006; Forth and Clyde Canal, Bankside 4 Nov 2006, 19 Jan and 22 May 2007 and Cramond 1 Sep 2007.

Green JNB	28 Jun 2006	Riccarton Pond, Edinburgh	4 Jan 2008	Gartmorn Dam (C)	KH

Green JUN	24 Aug 2002	Linlithgow Loch (West Lothian)	12 Apr 2008 17 May 2008 8 Sep 2008 11 Oct 2008	Falkirk stadium (F)	KH

Seen Falkirk Stadium 6 Jul 2007; taken into care Middlebank same day; back at Falkirk Stadium 21, 22 and 29 Sep 2007. Bred there in 2008 with Orange 3DFF and had 4 cygnets.

Orange 3BJC*	2 Nov 2002	Gartmorn Dam (C)	4 Jan 2008	Gartmorn Dam (C)	KH

A regular at Gartmorn Dam where present on several dates in 2003 and 2004. In 2005 bred there with unringed F and seen with 6 cygnets.

Orange 3CHT (lost) W12225	18 Sep 2004	Colzium, Kilsyth	4 Jan 2008	Gartmorn Dam (C)	KH

Seen Banton Loch 22 Jan and 12 Feb 2005; Gartmorn Dam 22 Feb, 26 Feb, 5 Mar, 19 Mar and 21 Mar 2005 and 19 Mar 2007 and Delph Pond, Tullibody 5 Apr 2007.

Orange 3CPV	10 Sep 2005	Lennoxtown (F)	4 Jan 2008	Gartmorn Dam (C)	KH

A well traveled individual. Seen Lennoxtown 2 Jan 2006; Gartmorn 19 and 31 Mar 2007 and River Leven, Dumbarton 4 Aug 2007.

Orange 3CZN	23 Sep 2006	Forth and Clyde Canal, Bankside, Falkirk (F)	4 Jan 2008	Gartmorn Dam (C)	KH

Seen Forth & Clyde Canal, Bankside 12 Jan 2007; Grangepans, Bo'ness 17 Feb 2007 and 3 Mar 2007.

Orange 3CZX	23 Sep 2006	Forth and Clyde Canal, Auchinstarry	4 Jan 2008	Gartmorn Dam (C)	KH

Seen Broadwood Loch, Cumbernauld 21 Apr 2007.

Orange 3DFF	22 Sep 2007	Falkirk Stadium (F)	12 Apr 2008 17 May 2008 8 Sep 2008 11 Oct 2008	Falkirk Stadium (F)	KH

Seen Falkirk stadium 29 Sep 2007. Bred there in 2008 with Green JUN and had 4 cygnets.

Metal W12294	19 Mar 2005	Gartmorn Dam (C)	4 Jan 2008	Gartmorn Dam (C)	KH

No known sightings in between probably due to lack of Darvic ring.

• BLACK-TAILED GODWIT (Icelandic race)

L: Orange flag above yellow ring R: Yellow ring above blue ring Metal ring FS 68010	11 Nov 2007	Moëze (Atlantic Coast) FRANCE	17 & 24 Apr 2008	Kinneil (F)	GFB

Also seen 12 Nov 2007 Les Mattes, Yves, FRANCE

SYSTEMATIC LIST

Codes - S, F and C refer to Stirling, Falkirk and Clackmannanshire Council Areas.

MUTE SWAN *Cygnus olor* (B,W)

Inland WeBS counts: 190 in Jan, 155 in Feb, 160 in Mar, 154 in Sep, 175 in Oct, 192 in Nov, 110 in Dec.

Forth Est (WeBS): 4 in Jan, 2 in Feb, 6 in Mar, 1 in Sep, 6 in Oct, 6 in Nov, 8 in Dec.

F   Ten Skinflats 2 Oct. 26 Underhill – R Carron, Forth/Clyde Canal 18 Oct and 16 Dec.

C   Breeding: pr and 4 Y Blackdevon Wetlands 19 Jun; pr and 2 Y Cambus Village Pool 19 Jun; pr and 6 Y Kersiepow Pond, Alva 1 Sep; no successful breeding at St Helen's Loch or Black Loch. Site max: 49 Gartmorn 27 Jan; 25 Blackdevon Wetlands 30 Jan.

S   Breeding: pr and 9 Y Polmaise Lagoons 22 May-Aug; pr and 1 Y Cambusmore 29 Jun; pr and 6 Y Ochlochy Pond, Dunblane 1 Sep; pr and 1 Y Doune Ponds; pr and 2 Y Cocksburn Res, BoA; no successful breeding at Vale of Coustry. Site max: 29 Airthrey Loch 14 Sep; 28 R Forth, Stirling 31 Mar; 10 Lake of Menteith 3 Dec.

WHOOPER SWAN *Cygnus cygnus* (W)

Inland WeBS counts: 18 in Jan, 28 in Feb, 21 in Mar, 0 in Sep, 10 in Oct, 39 in Nov, 17 in Dec.

Forth Est (WeBS): 65 in Oct, 43 in Nov.

F   Winter/spring: 4 Kinneil 12 Jan. Autumn/winter: 1 Skinflats 2 Oct, 2 there 10 Oct, 11 there 12 Oct, rising to 37 by 18 Oct and 65 on 26 Oct; 2 Kinneil 9 Oct; 33 Airth 18 Nov; 6 < Kinneil 22 Nov. 11 Darnrigg Moss 25 Dec.

C   Autumn/winter: 7 Blackdevon Wetlands 18 Oct; 1 Gartmorn Dam 27 Oct.

S   Winter/spring: 18 Carron Valley Res 14 Jan; 8 Upper Taylorton, R Forth 9 Feb. Autumn/winter: 3 Polmaise Lagoons 20 Oct; 10 Teith/Forth conf., Stirling 21 Oct, 36 there 16 Nov; 8 Cambus 28 Dec.

BEAN GOOSE *Anser fabalis* (W)

F   Slamannan plateau: 50 Bean Fm and 70 Wester Jawcraig Fm 4 Jan, 6 Easter Jawcraig 23 Jan, 80 Wester Lochgreen 30 Jan, 86 Bandominie 5 Feb, 70 Slamannan 21 Oct, 23 Hillend Fm 23 Oct (BGSG).

PINK-FOOTED GOOSE *Anser brachyrhynchus* (W)

Last spring record: 74 Alloa Inch 7 May (RSX). First autumn return: 20 Alloa Inch 9 Sep (RSX).

Forth Est (WeBS): 465 in Jan, 960 in Feb, 3235 in Mar, 1333 in Oct, 751 in Nov, 31 in Dec.

F   Winter/spring: 960 Skinflats 10 Feb. Autumn/winter: 1450 S Alloa 28 Oct.

C   Winter/spring: 600 Old Throsk Bridge 2 Feb; 1300 Cambus 19 Mar; 1600 Alloa Inch 9 Apr and 3 Mar; 1100 Tullibody Inch 2 May. Summer: 1 Blackdevon Wetlands 23 and 27 May; 1 Tullibody Inch 8 Jun.

S   Winter/spring: 1200 Flanders Moss 6 Jan; 2000 Lecropt 11 Jan; 200 Blair-drummond Moss 10 Feb; 3000 Thornhill Carse 9 Mar; 2500 Lake of Menteith 27 Mar; 1100 Thornhill Carse 9 Apr. Summer: 1 Cambusmore 28 July; 1 Lake of Menteith 4 Sep.

*GREATER WHITE-FRONTED GOOSE *Anser albifrons* (w)

F   Eleven (9 ad, 2 imm) birds of the Greenland race at Skinflats 28 Oct (MVB).

GREYLAG GOOSE *Anser anser* (b, W)

Forth Est (WeBS): 5 in Jan, 133 in Feb, 25 in Mar, 133 in Oct, 28 in Nov.

F   Winter/spring: 304 High Bonnybridge 4 Mar. Summer (feral): 131 Skinflats 11

Aug; 310 Blackness 14 Aug. Autumn/winter: 196 Skinflats 28 Oct; 116 Bonnybridge 6 Dec.

C   Winter/spring: 370 Alva 3 Jan. Autumn/winter: 450 Alloa Inch 9 Sep; 100 Gartmorn Dam 12 Nov.

S   Winter/spring: 595 L Coulter 11 Jan; 135 Cambuskenneth 21 Mar. Summer: 210 (incl Imms) N Third Res 27 Jun. Autumn/winter: 689 Bandeath, R Forth 11 Oct; 101 Killin 18 Nov; 305 L Coulter 6 Dec.

GREATER CANADA GOOSE *Branta canadensis* (b W)

Inland WeBS counts: 431 in Jan, 407 in Feb, 484 in Mar, 593 in Sep, 264 in Oct, 304 in Nov, 360 in Dec.

F   Max: 113 St. Helen's Loch, Bonnybridge 11 Jan, 99 there 6 Dec.

C   Max: 4 Gartmorn Dam 4 Aug; 90 Tullibody Inch 17 Sep.

S   Breeding: pr and 5 Y Cambusmore 20 May, 2 broods (4 and 2) there 11 Jun; pr and 4 Y North Third Res 27 Jun. Max: 200 Nether Carse 27 Mar; 204 Cambusmore 4 Sep; 260 L Venachar 16 Nov; 123 Lake of Menteith 3 Dec.

*BARNACLE GOOSE *Branta leucopsis* (w)

F   One Skinflats 11 Jan (AB). 7 Brackenlees Fm, Powfoulis 7 Dec (AB, GO).

S   Two Dochart Haughs 16 Jan (NB). 4 Easter Tarr, Ruskie 6 and 10 Feb (DT). 4 Cambushinnie 7 Feb (DOE). 1 Drip Moss 27 Feb (ACR). 6 Lower Auchinlay, Dunblane 30 Mar (CJP). 4 Drip Moss, Stirling 15 Nov (DMB). 2 Cambusbarron 23 Dec (GC).

*BRENT GOOSE *Branta bernicla* (w)

Four of pale-bellied race Skinflats on 20 Sep, with 11 there on 21-23 Sep (RP, DMB, GO *et al.*). 11 Kinneil 28 Sep with 7 there 27 Oct (DT, JRC).

COMMON SHELDUCK *Tadorna tadorna* (b, W)

Forth Est (WeBS): 1451 in Jan, 1311 in Feb, 858 in Mar, 1844 in Sep, 1986 in Oct, 1886 in Nov, 1394 in Dec.

F   Breeding: 8 Y Kinneil 13 Jul, and 3 new Y on 1 Aug. Moult flock: 3259 Grangemouth area 2 Aug (DMB); 691 Skinflats Pools 6 Jul.

C   Max: 84 Tullibody Inch 9 Feb; 64 Blackdevon Wetlands 19 Mar; 50 Alloa Inch 9 Apr.

S   One L Achray 17 Oct.

EURASIAN WIGEON *Anas penelope* (b, W)

Inland WeBS counts: 671 in Jan, 666 in Feb, 510 in Mar, 36 in Sep, 118 in Oct, 496 in Nov, 236 in Dec.

Forth Est (WeBS): 514 in Jan, 615 in Feb, 489 in Mar, 66 in Sep, 708 in Oct, 386 in Nov, 310 in Dec.

F   Winter/spring max: 207 Skinflats 10 Feb; 398 Kincardine Br 24 Feb; 65 Kinneil 3 Mar. Summer: 3 Skinflats 3 Jul. Autumn/winter max: 143 Skinflats 13 Dec.

C   Winter/spring site max: 100 Alloa Inch 2 Mar; 42 Blackdevon Wetlands 18 Mar. Summer: 4 Alloa Inch 7 May; pr Blackdevon Wetlands 9 May. Autumn/winter max: 50 Alloa 1 Nov; 85 Cambus Village Pool 6 Nov.

S   Winter/spring max: 80 Cambusmore 14 Jan; 105 Killin 16 Jan; 137 L Dochart/Lubhair 12 Feb; 163 Nether Carse 19 Feb. Summer: 2 L Dochart 21 June. Winter/spring max: 76 Killin 18 Nov.

*GADWALL *Anas strepera* (s, w)

F   One pr Kinneil 2 Feb (DT). 1 M Kincardine Br 9 Mar (MVB). 2 pr Skinflats 4 May (GO). 1 pr Kinneil 5 Dec (GO).

C   Two Gartmorn Dam 13 Mar (PMA). 1 pr Blackdevon Wetlands 14 Mar, 2 Apr and 3 May (CJH, NB, DMB). Cambus Pools: 4 pr 19 Mar, 2 on 23 Mar and 20 Apr, 1 pr on 9 May (DAC, ACC, PMA, NB). 3 Tullibody Inch 31 Mar (DMB).

S   One Airthrey Loch 16 Jan (ACC). 1 R Forth, Fallin 22 Nov (ACC). 1 pr N Third Res 28 Dec (BO).

EURASIAN TEAL   *Anas crecca*   (b, W)

Inland WeBS counts: 1089 in Jan, 1195 in Feb, 939 in Mar, 445 in Sep, 337 in Oct, 901 in Nov, 1009 in Dec.

Forth Est (WeBS): 1163 in Jan, 1123 in Feb, 823 in Mar, 440 in Sep, 1057 in Oct, 1322 in Nov, 1392 in Dec.

F   Winter/spring max: 450 Kinneil 2 Feb; 296 Skinflats 9 Mar. Autumn/winter max: 200 Kinneil 11 Oct; 550 Skinflats 13 Dec (record count for site).

C   Winter/spring max: 233 Kennetpans 6 Jan. Summer: 1 M Blackdevon Wetlands 9 May, 1 pr there 4 Jun. Autumn/winter max: 180 Cambus Pools 18 Sep; 132 Blackdevon Wetlands 28 Oct; 118 Tillicoultry 24 Dec.

S   Winter/spring max: 146 Fallin 10 Feb; 154 Blairdrummond Carse 9 Mar. Summer: pr Doune Lodge, BoD 26 Apr; 6 L Dochart 21 Jun. Autumn/winter max: 133 Lake of Menteith 3 Dec; 245 Fallin 31 Dec.

*GREEN-WINGED TEAL   *Anas carolinensis*

F   One M Kinneil 12 Jan, seen also in Dec 2007 (AET). 1 M Kinneil 5 Oct to 2009 (DT, GO, RS *et al.*). The record of the M moulting out of eclipse plumage on 5 Oct (DT) is the earliest recorded in Scotland (*Birds of Scotland Vol 3*). The latter, albeit possibly the same bird as the January bird, is the 6th record for the recording area. All of the above as well as the December 2006 record may refer to the same returning individual.

S   One M Cambusmore 17 Mar (JC, NB). This is the 5th record for the recording area.

MALLARD   *Anas platyrhynchos*   (B,W)

Inland WeBS counts: 2575 in Jan, 1780 in Feb, 1091 in Mar, 1473 in Sep, 1792 in Oct, 2137 in Nov, 1752 in Dec.

Forth Est (WeBS): 152 in Jan, 265 in Feb, 81 in Mar, 235 in Sep, 249 in Oct, 247 in Nov, 303 in Dec.

F   Breeding: F and 6 Y Carronshore 19 Jun. 22 Union Canal 22 Oct.

C   Breeding: F and 6 Y Gartmorn Dam 15 Apr; broods of 8 and 4 Blackdevon Wetlands 12 Jun; F and 6 Y Inglewood Pond, Alloa 1 Sep. Winter: 45 Dollar 28 Nov; 50 Gartmorn Dam 8 Dec.

S   Summer: 1 pr David Marshall Lodge, Aberfoyle 1 Apr. Max: 150 Airthrey Loch 14 Oct; 40 L Coulter 9 Feb.

NORTHERN PINTAIL   *Anas acuta*   (W)

Forth Est (WeBS): 88 in Jan, 87 in Feb, 51 in Mar, 61 in Oct, 86 in Nov, 61 in Dec.

F   Majority of above at Skinflats and Kinneil. Site max: 70 at Skinflats 10 Feb; 52 at Kinneil 19 Feb.

S   One Airthrey Loch 11 Jan (ACC).

NORTHERN SHOVELER   *Anas clypeata*   (p)

F   Kinneil: M 2 Feb; 2 on 28 Sep; 2 prs on 23 Nov, 1 pr on 25, 2 birds on 28 Nov; 3 birds on 5 Dec, 4 on 20 and 26 Dec (DT, GO, DAC). Skinflats: 1 on 17 Aug, 2 on 3 Sep (GO, RS, AB). First winter M St Helen's Loch 14 Oct (NB).

C   Blackdevon Wetlands: 1 pr 9 Jan, 2 M 31 Mar and 2 Apr, 1 M 14 Apr, 2 pr and 1 M 22 Apr, pr on 3 and 16 May (CJH, NB, DMB). Pr Tullibody Inch 31 Mar (DMB). F Cambus Village Pool 1 Sep (NB). Pr Alloa 28 Oct (DAC).

COMMON POCHARD   *Aythya ferina*   (W)

Inland WeBS counts: 47 in Jan, 35 in Feb, 12 in Mar, 2 in Sep, 6 in Oct, 32 in Nov, 10 in Dec.

F   One M Kinneil 24 Sep. 1 Forth/Clyde Canal, Bonnybridge 16 Nov.

C   Seven Gartmorn Dam 20 Jan, 2 on 12 Feb. 1 M Blackdevon Wetlands 19 Aug. 14 Gartmorn Dam 22 Nov.

S   Seventeen Carron Valley Res 14 Jan, 20 there 12 Feb. 11 Cambushinnie 14 Jan. 4

L Coulter 9 Feb. 4 Cambusmore 28 Jul. 11 Carron Valley Res 18 Nov.

TUFTED DUCK *Aythya fuligula* (B, W)

Inland WeBS counts: 379 in Jan, 277 in Feb, 463 in Mar, 223 in Sep, 396 in Oct, 405 in Nov, 224 in Dec.

F Max: 20 Kinneil House 15 Mar. Summer: 1 pr Skinflats 30 Mar; 1 pr Kinneil 10 Jul.

C Max: 238 Gartmorn Dam 22 Mar.

S Breeding: 6 ad and 8 Y Carron Valley Res 16 Jun; broods of 2, 5 and 9 Cambusmore 28 Jul. Max: 28 Airthrey Loch 3 Jan; 63 Vale of Coustry 19 Mar; 60 Lake of Menteith 3 Dec; 37 Carron Valley Res 20 Dec.

GREATER SCAUP *Aythya marina* (s, w)

Forth Est (WeBS): 4 in Jan, 11 in Mar, 1 in Sep, 21 in Oct, 26 in Nov, 40 in Dec.

F Kinneil: up to 5 in Jan; up to 6 in Feb; up to 5 in Mar; 14 on 4 May; 1 on 28 Jun; up to 4 in Jul; up to 2 in Aug; up to 15 in Sep; up to 20 in Oct; up to 31 in Nov; up to 35 in Dec (AB, DAC, GO *et al.*). Skinflats: 1 on 5 Aug; 2 on 30 Sep; max of 9 in Oct, 1 on 24 Nov (CJP, GO, MVB *et al.*).

S One M Airthrey Loch 26 Jan to 6 Feb (CJP, ACC).

*LESSER SCAUP *Aythya affinis*

S One M Vale of Coustry 19 Mar to 17 Apr (NB, AL). This bird was accepted by BBRC and is the forth record for the area.

COMMON EIDER *Somateria mollissima* (w, s)

Forth Est (WeBS): 2 in Jan, 18 in Feb, 26 in Mar, 5 in Oct, 46 in Nov, 72 in Dec.

F Kinneil: 1 on 5 Jan; 4 on 2 Mar; 20 (10 M, 10 F) on 29 Mar; max of 6 M on 3 Jun; 4 on 18 Jul; max of 10 on 23 Sep; max of 11 on 5 in Oct; max of 66 on 18 Nov and 80 on 26 Dec (DAC, DT, AB, GO). Skinflats: 18 on 10 Feb; 23 on 9 Mar (MVB). 2 Kincardine 6 Jan, 10 on 17 Mar and 3 on 18 May (MVB, DMB, ACC).

C Two Kennetpans 18 May (DMB).

LONG-TAILED DUCK *Clangula hyemalis* (w)

F Imm Skinflats 15-24 Nov (MVB, GO, AB).

S Imm/F Carron Valley Res 21 Dec (CJP).

*COMMON SCOTER *Melanitta nigra*

F F Kinneil 18 Nov (DT). This is the 13th record for the recording aera since systematic recording began in 1974.

COMMON GOLDENEYE *Bucephala clangula* (W)

Inland WeBS counts: 428 in Jan, 394 in Feb, 483 in Mar, 0 in Sep, 59 in Oct, 333 in Nov, 350 in Dec.

Forth Est (WeBS): 66 in Jan, 71 in Feb, 29 in Mar, 3 in Oct, 18 in Nov, 52 in Dec.

F Max: 19 Kinneil 6 Jan; 8 Drumbowie 11 Jan; 14 Airth 11 Feb; 31 Black Loch 4 Mar; 18 Skinflats 8 Apr.

C Max: 73 Gartmorn Dam 27 Jan; 14 Silverhills Pond, Alva 4 Feb; 54 Cambus 9 Feb; 43 R Devon, Tullibody 20 Feb.

S Max: 37 Carron Valley Res 14 Jan; 124 Lake of Menteith 11 Mar; 38 L Dochart/Lubhair 1 Nov.

RED-BREASTED MERGANSER *Mergus serrator* (B, W)

Forth Est (WeBS): 36 in Jan, 40 in Feb, 22 in Mar, 68 in Sep, 57 in Oct, 76 in Nov, 84 in Dec.

F Majority of above at Kinneil; site max: 95 on 5 Oct. 15 Skinflats 13 Dec.

C Two M Cambus 4 Feb, 6 on 19 Mar; 1 on 8 Apr. 1 M Delph Pool, Tullibody 4 Feb. Two R Devon, Alva 2 Apr. 12 Alloa landfill ponds 1 Nov.

S Three R Forth, Craigforth 6 Jan, 5 on 9 Feb, 2 on 4 Mar, 1 on 14 Mar, 1 on 25 Dec. Two Blairdrummond Safari Park 22 Feb. 1 Carron Valley Res 15 Mar. 4 Allanwater, Kinbuck 6 May. 2 L Katrine 13 Jun.

GOOSANDER *Mergus merganser* (B, W)
Inland WeBS counts: 132 in Jan, 134 in Feb, 94 in Mar, 61 in Sep, 52 in Oct, 65 in Nov, 97 in Dec.
Forth Est (WeBS): 3 in Feb, 22 in Mar, 28 in Sep, 13 in Oct, 9 in Nov, 4 in Dec.

F   Breeding: F and 8 Y R Carron, Carronshore 19 Jun; F and 6 Y Kinneil 10 Jul. Max: 11 Kinneil 29 Aug.
C   Max: 15 R Devon, Alva 3 Jan; 36 Cambus 19 Mar.
S   Breeding: 2 F and 10 Y Allan Water, Dunblane 11 May; F and 9 Y Cambusmore 11 Jun. Max: 16 Airthrey Loch 25 Jan; 15 Allan-Teith conf., R Forth 9 Feb; 23 Aberfoyle 7 Jun; 27 L Ard 18 Jul; 28 L Achray 14 Sep.

*WILLOW PTARMIGAN (RED GROUSE) *Lagopus lagopus* (B, W)
S   Sixty Cringate Muir 10 Feb (CJP). Also recorded from BoD, L Coulter, L Lubnaig, Beinn Uird (DOE, ABu, DK).

BLACK GROUSE *Tetrao tetrix* (B, W)
S   Records from Cringate Muir; Callander; L Katrine; L Ard Forest (DOE, ABu, CJP).

GREY PARTRIDGE *Perdix perdix* (B, W)
F   Skinflats/Powfoulis: 2 pr 23 Feb and 10 Apr, pr in Mar; max of 14 on 10 Oct (GO, RDZ, AB *et al.*).
C   Two Cambus 26 Apr (DK). 2 Blackdevon 4 Jun and 11 Aug (CJH). 1 Menstrie 20 Sep (RSX). 6 Tullibody/Alva 29 Oct and 15 Nov, with 9 there 7 Dec (DAC).
S   Six Lecropt 5 Jan (DOE). 2 Doune 2 Nov (DOE).

*COMMON QUAIL *Coturnix coturnix*
S   One Thornhill 7 and 17 Jul (DT).

COMMON PHEASANT *Phasianus colchicus* (B, W)
Very large numbers released on shooting estates, otherwise widespread but in small numbers.
F   18 Kinneil 28 Dec (record count for site; GO).

* RED-THROATED DIVER *Gavia stellata* (b, w)
F   Kinneil: 1 on 3 Jan, 2 on 6 Jan, 3 on 29 Mar, 1 on 13 Sep, 2 on 21 Sep, singles on 5 Oct, 18 Nov and 13 Dec (JRC, DT, JT).
S   Trossachs: pr at undisclosed site 25 May (DAC).

LITTLE GREBE *Tachybaptus ruficollis* (B, w)
Inland WeBS counts: 83 in Jan, 82 in Feb, 51in Mar, 128 in Sep, 108 in Oct, 77 in Nov, 63 in Dec.
F   Site max: 13 Drumbowie Res 12 Sep; 11 Black Loch 12 Sep; 5 St. Helen's Loch 12 Sep.
C   Breeding: 2 Y Clackmannan 6 Jun; ad and 2 Y Gartmorn Dam 14 Aug; pr and 4 Y Blackdevon Wetlands 19 Aug; ad and 1 Y Aberdona 1 Sep. Max: 8 Silverhills Pond, Kersiepow 1 Sep.
S   Breeding: 1 pr David Marshall Lodge, Aberfoyle 1 Apr; 8 ad and 4 Y Cambusmore GP 28 Jul; 1 Y Polmaise Lagoons 21 Aug. Max: 19 Cambusmore 4 Sep; 19 L Dochart 8 Sep (site record); 17 L Lubnaig 22 Sep; 14 L Voil 12 Feb; 8 L Ard 18 Jan; 7 Vale of Coustry 11 Sep; 6 Carron Valley Res 12 Feb.

GREAT CRESTED GREBE *Podiceps cristatus* (b, W)
Inland WeBS counts: 5 in Jan, 16 in Feb, 29 in Mar, 32 in Sep, 18 in Oct, 14 in Nov, 14 in Dec.
Forth Est (WeBS): 7 in Jan, 2 in Feb, 2 in Mar, 9 in Sep, 14 in Oct, 10 in Nov, 25 in Dec.
F   Site max: 39 Kinneil 23 Jul.
C   Site max: 5 Gartmorn Dam 9 Jul.
S   Breeding: 2 prs Cambusmore, none fledged; pr Vale of Coustry 5 Apr. Max: 24 Lake of Menteith 4 Sep (site record).

*RED-NECKED GREBE *Podiceps grisegena*
F   One Blackness 18 Oct (MA). This is the 14th record for the recording area since 1974.
S   One Cocksburn Res, BOA 26 Nov (ACR). This is the 15th record for the recording area.
*SLAVONIAN GREBE *Podiceps auritus*
S   One L Coulter 14 Oct (NB). 1 Lake of Menteith 17 Oct (NB). 1 Cambusmore 21 Nov (NB). These constitute the 16th to 18th inland records for the recording area.
*NORTHERN GANNET *Morus bassanus* (p)
F   Two Imm Skinflats and 1 Imm Kinneil 13 Sep (ACC, DT). 2 Imm Kinneil 24 and 28 Sep (DT). 15 Imm Skinflats 10 Oct (AB). 2 Imm Kinneil 22 Oct (DMB) and 7 there 27 Oct (JRC). 2 Imm Skinflats 18 Oct (CJP).
S   Two Imm flew up Allan Water, Dunblane 22 Sep (CJP).
GREAT CORMORANT *Phalacrocorax carbo* (S, W)
     Comparatively small numbers. An update on the S Alloa roost is needed.
     Inland WeBS counts: 73 in Jan, 75 in Feb, 47 in Mar, 48 in Sep, 77 in Oct, 78 in Nov, 56 in Dec.
     Forth Est (WeBS): 77 in Jan, 62 in Feb, 73 in Mar, 104 in Sep, 68 in Oct, 31 in Nov, 28 in Dec.
F   Twenty-five Skinflats 14 Sep.
S   Max: 18 Lake of Menteith 12 Nov; 14 Fallin, R Forth 14 Sep; 11 Carron Valley Res 18 Nov; 10 Airthrey 25 Jan.
*EUROPEAN SHAG *Phalacrocorax aristotelis*
F   One Kinneil 2, 17 and 24 Aug and 14 Sep (DH, DT, JRC).
GREY HERON *Ardea cinerea* (B,W)
     Inland WeBS counts: 92 in Jan, 71 in Feb, 64 in Mar, 94 in Sep, 86 in Oct, 89 in Nov, 55 in Dec.
     Forth Est (WeBS): 21 in Jan, 32 in Feb, 6 in Mar, 66 in Sep, 38 in Oct, 41 in Nov, 36 in Dec.
F   Breeding: 40 birds / 5+ nests Kinneil Woods 6 Mar. Max: 30 Skinflats and 10 Kinneil 14 Sep.
C   Max: 13 Blackgrange 27 Oct; 12 Alva floods 15 Nov; 12 Dollar – Tillicoultry, R Devon 23 Sep.
S   Max: 11 L Coulter 9 Feb; 8 Vale of Coustry 26 Oct.
*WHITE STORK
S   1 > SE at Fallin 10 May (RHD).
     This is the 2nd record of a bird considered as wild for the recording area, the first one dating back to May 1982, although the picture is complicated by feral populations, such as north-east England.
EURASIAN SPOONBILL *Platalea leucorodia*
F   Two ad Kinneil 2 Jul to 29 Aug (JFo, RS, GO *et al.*). This is the 6th record for the recording area.
RED KITE *Milvus milvus* (b ,W)
F   One Kinneil 25 Nov (EG).
C   One Ben Cleuch 10 May (CJP).
S   Breeding: 20 prs laid eggs, 13 successfully fledging 31 Y (DOE, DA). Max at Argaty, BoD: 50 on 4 Dec (DOE). Away from BoD: 1 Lecropt 5-6 Jan; 1 Dunblane 31 Mar and 25 May; 1 Airthrey Loch and BoA 10 and 19 Apr; up to 3 Callander in Apr/May; 1 Sheriffmuir 6 May; 1 Stirling 15 Jun; up to 2 BOA/Cornton Jul/Aug; 1 Kilmahog 26 Oct; 1 Lecropt 12 Nov; 1 L Venachar 16 Nov.
WHITE-TAILED EAGLE *Haliaeetus albicilla*
S   At least one imm from the Fife reintroduction scheme seen Argaty, BoD 23 Jan

(DOE); near Blairdrummond 3 Feb, 16 Apr, 30 Oct (GEL, KS); 1 Doune 10 Jul (DOE); 1 Callander 18 Dec (DOE).

*HEN HARRIER *Circus cyaneus* (b, w)

F   One Darnrigg Moss 7 Jan and 25 Dec (TF).

S   One M Dumyat 6 Feb. 1 Strath Gartney, L Katrine 6 and 19 Feb, and 1 Beinn Bhreac 12 Feb (ABu). 3 Flanders Moss 18 Feb and 1 Nether Carse 19 Feb (ACR). 1 M Kinbuck 25 Feb (NB). 1 Blairdrummond Moss 4 and 31 Mar, and 1 Flanders Moss 16 Mar (ACR). 1 M Gleann Dubh 11 May (HY). 1 F Ben Each 3 Aug (CJP). 1 F/Imm L Coulter 6 and 7 Dec (NB).

EURASIAN SPARROWHAWK *Accipiter nisus* (B, W)

F   Records from: Dunmore Woods, Kinneil House; Skinflats; Blackness; Bonnybridge, Limerigg.

C   Records from: Alva; Menstrie; Tullibody; Tillicoultry; Cambus; Gartmorn; Dollar.

S   Records from: Fallin; Stirling; Airthrey; BoA; Blairdrummond; Drumloist and Lundie, BoD (bred); Dunblane; Sheriffmuir; Deanston (bred); Doune (bred); Callander; Carron Valley Res; L Doine; Lake of Menteith; L Ard Forest; Lanrick.

COMMON BUZZARD *Buteo buteo* (B,W)

Breeding: 142 occupied sites; of 76 prs confirmed to lay eggs, 67 fledged 110 Y and 5 prs failed (DOE, DA).

GOLDEN EAGLE *Aquila chrysaetos* (b, w)

S   One Imm G Finglas 21 Jan (RR). 2 L Katrine area Jan/Feb (ABu). 2 Monachyle Glen 20 Apr (DK). 4 G Lochay 3 May; ad F and imm M there 27 Jun (GS, KDS, AC). 1 BoD 11 May (DOE). 1 Balquhidder Glen 13 Jul (DOE). 1 Tyndrum 29 Jul (WM).

OSPREY *Pandion haliaetus* (B)

F   One Kinneil 28 Aug (DG).

S   Breeding: of 15 prs 14 laid eggs, 13 successfully fledging 26 Y (DOE, RAB, DA). First records: 1 L Katrine 18 and 27 Feb; 1 Lake of Menteith 25 Feb. Other records from: Duke's Pass on 1 Apr; L Venachar on 1 Apr, 5 May, 4 Sep; Doune in Apr and Jun (2); Lake of Menteith Apr to Jul; Blairdrummond on 18 Apr (2); Carron Valley Res Apr and Jun (2); Touch Res on 12 Sep; L Venachar on 14 Aug.

COMMON KESTREL *Falco tinnunculus* (B,W)

F   Records from: Plean; Kincardine Br; Skinflats; Kinneil; Falkirk.

C   Records from: Blairlogie; Blackdevon Wetlands; Tullibody; Alva; Gartmorn Dam.

S   Four prs BoD; 2 prs N of Callander. Other records: Abbey Craig; Airthrey Loch; Dunblane; Lecropt; Cambuskenneth; Stirling; Blairdrummond; Flanders Moss; Carron Valley Res; L Achray.

*MERLIN *Falco columbarius* (b?, w)

F   One Kinneil 11 Jan (BRG). 1 F Skinflats 19 Jan and 10 Feb (AB, MVB). 1 Airth 11 Feb (DMB). 1 Kinneil 19 Feb (GFB). 2 Skinflats 26 Oct, 1 on 15 Nov (MVB). 1 Kinneil 25 Nov (ACR). 1 F/Imm Skinflats 7 Dec (AB, GO).

S   One F Lecropt 5 Jan (DOE). One M Doune 23 Jan (DOE). 1 Gleann Dubh 8 Jun (HY). 1 Stirling 20 Oct (RS).

PEREGRINE FALCON *Falco peregrinus* (B, W)

F   One Skinflats 19 Sep. 1 Kinneil 22 Aug, 24 Sep, 2 and 16 Nov and 24 Dec.

S   Two BoD 6 Jan. 1 Cairnoch Hill, Carron Valley 19 Jan. 1 M Argaty, BoD 26 Jan. 1 L Coulter 3 Feb. 2 Airthrey 2 May; 1 Lake of Menteith 8 Jul; 1 Tyndrum 29 Jul; 1 Fallin 2 Aug.

WATER RAIL *Rallus aquaticus* (b, w)

F   Kinneil: single 6 Jan, 3 on 12-13 Sep, 1 on 24 Sep and 2 Nov and 2 on 13 Dec (DT,

DMB, AB, JRC). Skinflats: 1 on 9 Mar, in Aug and on 17 and 24 Nov (MVB, AB, RS *et al.*).

C One Gartmorn Dam 14 Aug (CJH). 1 Blackdevon Wetlands 29 Nov (DMB).

S One R Teith, Lecropt 6 Jan (CJP). One Airthrey Loch 21 Jan (ACC).

COMMON MOORHEN *Gallinula chloropus* (B,W)

 Inland WeBS counts: 108 in Jan, 102 in Feb, 94 in Mar, 88 in Sep, 100 in Oct, 129 in Nov, 97 in Dec.

F Breeding: 3 ad and 14 Juv Kinneil 23 Jul. Max: 6 Kinneil House 15 Mar; 22 Underhill – R Carron, Forth/Clyde Canal 12 Sep; 8 Millhall Res, Polmont 15 Nov; 29 Callendar Park, Falkirk 15 Dec.

C Breeding: 3 pr Blackdevon Wetlands 24 Jun; 2 broods of 2 and 3 Cambus Pools 19 Aug. Max: 11 Gartmorn Dam 12 Oct.

S Breeding: 3 Y Polmaise Lagoons 17 Jul, 2 Y still 21 Aug; 2 Imm L Dochart 8 Sep; 3 Imm St Helen's Loch 12 Sep; 3 Imm Castle Park, Stirling 12 Sep; 1 Imm Drumbowie Loch 12 Sep. Max: 12 Airthrey Loch Jan/Feb; 5 Vale of Coustry and 5 Blairdrummond Safari Park 24 Nov.

COMMON COOT *Fulica atra*   (B, W)

 Inland WeBS counts: 339 in Jan, 184 in Feb, 146 in Mar, 54 in Sep, 115 in Oct, 117 in Nov, 53 in Dec.

F Breeding: 2 ad and 2 Imm Braeface Pond 23 Jun.

C Breeding: pr Blackdevon Wetlands 24 Jun. Max: 186 Gartmorn Dam 27 Jan.

S Breeding: 1 pr and 3 Y Cambusmore 28 Jul; 1 pr and 2 Imm Castle Park, Stirling 12 Sep. Site max: 76 Airthrey Loch 21 Jan; 39 Lake of Menteith in Feb and Nov. 6 E Frew, R Forth 19 Feb.

EURASIAN OYSTERCATCHER *Haematopus ostralegus* (B, W)

 WeBS Forth estuary peaks were 298 in Feb and 167 in Nov.

F Return inland: 17 birds at Skinflats on 28 Feb increased to 40 by 18 Apr, with 66 there on 12 Jun, 74 on 29 Aug and 45 on 13 Sep. 123 birds were at Kinneil on 29 Aug and 75 at the Avon mouth on 2 Nov.

S Return inland: 1 at Craigforth 12 Jan increased to 56 by 9 Feb and 129 on 27 Feb. A small flock seemed to overwinter with 15 birds there on 22 Nov and 13 Dec and 8 still into early Jan 2009. Further upstream 3 birds were at the Br of Frew-E Frew stretch on 29 Jan. 10 Airthrey L 27 Jan. Vale of Coustry held 73 birds on 12 Feb, increasing to 229 by 22 Feb. Elsewhere 1 BoA 12 Feb, 10 Cocksburn Res 14 Feb increasing to ca. 30 by 5 Mar, 61 Ashfield 15 Feb with 79 there 20 Mar. 1 L. Dochart and 6 Lochearnhead 17 Feb; ca. 30 Carse of Lecropt 19 Feb; 18 Fallin waste disposal site 9 Mar; 35 Ardeonoig, L Tay 14 Mar. Pr at North Lodge roundabout, BoA 2 Jun.

RINGED PLOVER *Charadrius hiaticula* (b, W)

 WeBS estuary peaks were 1 in Mar and 34 in Sep.

F As in 2006 and 2007, smaller numbers than before. 6 Kinneil 12 Feb with 2 there 5 May and 5 Jul, 5 on 27 Jul, 8 on 14 Sep, while 8 on 5 Oct included a leucistic bird. 2 Kincardine Br 18 May. A pr at the Grangemouth oil refinery in late May was believed on a nest. 30 Skinflats 20 May, 15 on 22 Aug and 16 on Carron mouth 14 Sep. 16 Blackness 12 Oct.

C Two Cambus Pools 8 Apr. 50 Kennetpans 2 Sep.

S Gart GP, Callander held between 4 to 10 birds between 28 Feb and 21 Apr. A single there 12 May was absent by 4 Jun, suggesting poor breeding success.

EUROPEAN GOLDEN PLOVER *Pluvialis apricaria* (B, W)

 WeBS estuary peaks were 82 in Feb and 977 in Oct.

F Numbers low during the first part but higher in second part of year. Ca. 150 Kinneil 6 Jan increased to ca. 200 by 26 Jan with 2 remaining 3 Apr. Return to the estuary: 2 Blackness 1 Jul was followed by 1 Skinflats 7 Jul, then 15 there on 9 Aug with 11 on 4 Sep, 40 on 18 Sep, 95 on 14 Oct and 730 during the Forth WeBS count of 26 Oct. At Kinneil 210 there 24 Sep and 250 11 Oct, 150 on 21 Oct and 25 on 24 Dec. 560 Powfoulis 10 Oct.

S   Thornhill Carse: 5 Littleward 9 Mar & 70 Myme Fm 7 Apr. 1 Callander 26 Jul.

GREY PLOVER *Pluvialis squatarola* (W)

F   One Kinneil 30 Aug. 22 Skinflats area 19 Sep, 16 on 26 Oct with 3 there on 10 Dec. 2 Kincardine Br 13 Dec.

NORTHERN LAPWING *Vanellus vanellus* (B, W)

     WeBS estuary peaks were 632 in Jan and 1562 in Sep.

F   As in 2007 numbers were generally low again. Kinneil: ca. 350 1 Jan was followed by 772 on 8 Jan and 200 on 12 Feb. 50 on 5 Jul increased to 200 on 27 Jul, then 360 on 29 Aug, ca. 650 on 13 Sep, 200 on 23 Sep and 200 on 25 Nov. Skinflats: 117 on 6 Jan, 30 there 25 Jun, 50 on 31 Jul, 560 on 29 Aug, 250 on 13 Sep, 964 in the general area (WeBS) on 14 Sep and 200 on 18 Nov. Elsewhere 2 ads with 2 downy Y Carronshore to Skinflats path 11 Jun.

C   Tullibody Inch: 450 on 13 Jan and 1270 there 16 Aug. 8 on Alloa Inch 7 May. 4 on pools at Blackdevon Wetlands 30 Jan rose to 28 by 27 Feb (1 AOT), max in Mar 52 and 8 AOT in May; 55 birds on 9 Sep, 40 on 21 Oct and 80 on 1 Nov. 25 R Devon, Alva 17 Feb; 20 Woodland Park and Drove Rd, Alva 22 Apr. 200 nr Menstrie 6 Oct. 80 Blackgrange and 150 Cambus 27 Oct with 70 there 21 Nov. 111 Blackgrange 22 Nov.

S   Two Doune 3 Jan. 156 L Coulter 9 Feb with 112 there 4 Mar. 200 Vale of Coustry 10 Feb. 165 Gart GP 28 Jul. R Forth: Fallin-Cambus 150 on 27 Oct; 111 Up Taylorton-Fallin 22 Nov; 133 Br of Frew-E Frew 25 Nov.

RED KNOT *Calidris canutus* (W)

     WeBS estuary peaks were 781 in Jan and 597 in Dec.

F   Airth-Dunmore: 300 on 11 Feb with 1500 there 24 Feb. Kinneil: 1000 on 12 Feb. First returning bird 6 Jun, 8 by 27 Jul, 50 on 1 Aug, 19 on 14 Aug, 60 on 14 Sep, ca. 150 on 28 Sep, 80 on 11 Oct and 700 on 24 Dec. Skinflats: 140 on 29 Aug, 210 on 26 Oct, 237 on 13 Dec and a good count of 5000 on mudflats on 28 Dec.

SANDERLING *Calidris alba*

F   Two Kinneil 6 Jan and 4 there 16 Jul (JRC, GO, RS).

PECTORAL SANDPIPER *Calidris melanotos*

C   Juv Tullibody Inch 26 Sep (GW). This is the third record of this species for the recording area since 1974.

CURLEW SANDPIPER *Calidris ferruginea* (p)

F   Skinflats: 2 juvs on 31 Aug and 2 Sep. 5 on 13 Sep and 8 on 14 to 18 Sep; 2 on 16 Sep. Kinneil: 5 juvs 13 Sep with 2 there 14 Sep and 18 Sep. 1 Kennetpans 14 Sep.

Autumn passage, area summary (minimum number/half month)							
Jul		Aug		Sep		Oct	
0	0	0	2	14	10	0	0

DUNLIN *Calidris alpina* (b?, W)

     WeBS estuary peaks were 3733 in Jan and 5097 in Dec.

F   Kinneil: ca. 500 on 6 Jan with 400 there 12 Feb down to 47 on 3 Mar; ca. 400 on 18 Nov rose to 1000 on 24 Dec. Skinflats: 1855 on 6 Jan rose to 2200 on 10 Feb. 2 on 12 Jun, 4 on 3 Jul rose to 60 on 13 Sep, 1655 on 26 Oct, 2500 on 15 Nov, 3560 on 13 Dec and 2000+ on 28 Dec. Elsewhere 1 St. Helen's Loch, Bonnybridge 3 Nov.

RUFF *Philomachus pugnax* (w, p)

F   As in 2006 and 2007 one bird overwintered at Skinflats where it was seen 4 Jan. Either a passage or the same bird in summer plumage was at Kinneil on 24 and

28 Apr and 5 May (RS, GFB, AET). Autumn passage started at Skinflats with 3 birds on 13 to 16 Aug, 5 on 17 Aug, increasing to 8 on 19 Aug before dropping to 4 by 29 Aug with a single(s) seen on several dates up to 22 Sep (CT, RS, GG, AB, MVB, RD, GO, GFB, DOE, AB). At Kinneil 3 birds on 23 Aug, 13 and 14 Sep dropped to 2 on 24 and 28 Sep, with an ad on 3, 5 11 and 12 Oct (GFB, AB, ACC, DT, RD). Elsewhere a single was at Strathavon Fm, Slamannan 4 Oct (TF). An overwintering bird again at Skinflats 26 Dec (RS).

Autumn passage, area summary (minimum number/half month)							
Jul		Aug		Sep		Oct	
0	0	5	11	7	3	2	0

JACK SNIPE *Lymnocryptes minimus* (w)

F 1 Skinflats 14 Jan. 3 St. Helen's Loch, Bonnybridge 11 Jan with 1 there 4 Mar. 2 Feughlin Res, Carron Br 11 Jan. 2 Kinneil 19 Feb. 2 Skinflats on saltmarsh 7 Dec; 2 there at Muirdyke Burn 12 Dec and 1 Kinneil 18 Dec (RS, NB, DT, AB, DMB).

S 2 Netherton Marsh, Carse of Lecropt 11 Jan and 1 on the carse 21 Dec (DT, DOE).

COMMON SNIPE *Gallinago gallinago* (B,W)

WeBS estuary peaks were 6 in Jan and 16 in Nov.

F Six Kinneil 6 Jan with 7 there 26 Jan, 5 on 14 Sep and 9 on 24 Sep. 38 St. Helen's Loch, Bonnybridge 11 Jan with 26 there 15 Feb, 13 on 4 Mar, 12 on 12 Sep, 63 on 3 Nov and 7 on 6 Dec. 6 Faughlin Res, Carron Br 14 Oct. 9 Muirdyke Burn, Skinflats 7 Dec.

C Three Cambus Village Pools 30 Jul. 5 Blackdevon Wetlands 1 Nov. 12 Aberdona Pond 6 Nov.

S River Forth: 19 at Carse of Lecropt, 50 on Stirling-Upper Taylorton stretch, 19 between Teith and Allan confluences all on 12 Jan. 32 Upper Taylorton-Fallin 20 Jan, 30 Stirling-Upper Taylorton 9 Feb with 37 there 9 Mar. 15 Br of Frew-E Frew 27 Mar with 11 there 28 Oct. 7 Teith-Allan confluences 12 Oct and 22 Stirling-Upper Taylorton 16 Nov. Elsewhere 37 Netherton Marsh, Carse of Lecropt 12 Jan. 12 Allan, county boundary-Ashfield 12 Jan. 7 Cambusmore 14 Jan with 28 there 27 Feb, 12 on 17 Mar and 6 on 11 Nov. 6 Hillhead Pond, Thornhill 19 Mar. 6 Blackwater Marshes, L Venachar 16 Nov. In breeding season: 1 drumming Sheriffmuir 16 Jun.

EURASIAN WOODCOCK *Scolopax rusticola* (B, W)

Grossly under-recorded during the breeding season.

F Singles Darnrig Moss former opencast site 28 Jan and Drumbowie Res, Denny 6 Dec.

C One crossed road nr Dollarbeg 7 Feb. Singles R Devon Alva-Menstrie 24 Mar and R Forth nr Alloa 6 Dec.

S Five at Teapot, Kinlochard 16 Jan with 1 there 30 Jan. 22 Brenachoile Lodge, L Katrine 16 Jan. 2 Lundie, BoD 17 Jan. 5 Bad Dearg, L Ard 18 Jan with 1 there 22 Jan. 6 Cambusbarron 19 Jan. Singles Bigg Wood, Dunblane 27 Jan; Stronmacnair, L Ard Forest 28 Jan; L Coulter 3 Feb; Barr Wood, Bannockburn 3 Feb; Touch Hills 10 Feb; R Forth, Stirling-Upper Taylorton 9 Mar; Stable Point, L of Menteith 11 Mar; Lundie, BoD 21 Mar; Tom an t-Seallaidh, Duke's Pass, Aberfoyle 1 Apr; 2 Cobleland, Aberfoyle 7 Jun. Single L Rusky 11 Nov and 1 flushed by Hen Harrier L Coulter 6 Dec. R Forth: Br of Frew-E Frew 9 Dec; 2 Ladylands-Br of Frew 11 Dec and 1 Stirling-Upper Taylorton 13 Dec.

BLACK-TAILED GODWIT *Limosa limosa* (W)

WeBS estuary peaks were low with 62 in Jan and 453 in Sep.

F Present most year in Grangemouth area, except January. 69 R Forth, Airth-

Dunmore 11 Feb. Monthly peaks at Kinneil: 80 in Mar, 91 in Apr, 73 in May, 60 in Jun, 187 in Jul, 325 in Aug, 307 in Sep, 276 in Oct, 40 in Nov and 187 in Dec. Much smaller numbers at Skinflats, where monthly peaks: 1 in Feb, 15 in Mar, 68 in Apr, 1 in May , 9 in Jul, 17 in Aug and 18 in Sep.

C   Low numbers upstream of Kincardine Br this year. 10 Cambus area 19 Mar. 6 Blackdevon Wetlands 18 Apr with 8 there in breeding plumage 4 Jun and 5 on 12 Jun.

BAR-TAILED GODWIT *Limosa lapponica* (W)

WeBS estuary peaks were 33 in Jan and 40 in Sep.

F   Numbers were again low at Kinneil and the species virtually absent from Skinflats. 105 Kinneil 8 Jan with c. 115 there 2 Feb, 9 on 28 Jun, 10 on 27 Jul, 80 on 14 Sep, and 150 on 24 Dec. Singles Skinflats 6 Apr and 24 Nov. 14 Kincardine Br 14 Sep.

C   5 Kennetpans 13 Dec.

WHIMBREL *Numenius phaeopus* (p)

F   Spring: 1 Skinflats 18 Apr with 2 there 26 Apr and 5 on 5 May. Singles Kinneil 6 and 18 May (AB, GO, AET, DT, GFB). Autumn: 2 Kinneil 4 Jul, singles 8 and 10 Jul, 3 on 23 Jul, rising to 10 on 29 Jul, then singles on 1 and 2 Aug, 3 on 8 Aug, singles 16 and 22 Aug, 10 on 25 Aug and 1 on 30 Aug. Skinflats: singles on 1 and 3 Sep, 2 on 14 Sep, singles on 22 Sep and 2 Oct. 2 Kincardine Br 14 Sep (GO, DT, RDZ, GFB, ACC, AB, MVB).

Autumn passage, area summary (minimum number/half month)							
Jul		Aug		Sep		Oct	
2	10	3	10	4	2	2	0

EURASIAN CURLEW *Numenius arquata* (B, W)

WeBS estuary peaks were 1088 in Jan and 1195 in Oct.

F   Skinflats Est: 538 on 6 Jan with 502 there 10 Feb, 398 on 14 Sep, 778 on 26 Oct and 393 on 15 Nov. 200 Kinneil 14 Sep and 100 there 23 Sep. 180 Old Throsk Br 2 Feb.

C   177 Cambus Village Pools area 3 Jan with 293 on 4 Feb, 153 on 3 Nov and 225 on 21 Nov. 260 Tullibody Inch 13 Jan. 180 Kennetpans 9 Mar. 256 Blackgrange 22 Nov.

S   R Forth: ca. 150 Upper Taylorton-Fallin 20 Jan; 225 Fallin-Cambus 21 Nov; 256 Upper Taylorton-Fallin 22 Nov and 226 Fallin-Cambus 28 Dec. Ca. 215 Carse of Lecropt 2 Mar and ca. 180 there 8 Mar. 181 R Teith, Wester Row-Forth conf 9 Mar.

*SPOTTED REDSHANK *Tringa erythropus* (p)

F   Single Skinflats and 29 Feb, 8, 28 and 29 Mar and 6 Apr (AB, BRG, GO, RS). Single Kinneil 16 and 27 Apr, 4 May and 5 May when moulting (RS, GO) but apparently present throughout from 1 Jan to 14 Apr (BRG).

COMMON REDSHANK *Tringa totanus* (B, W)

WeBS estuary peaks were 1923 in Mar and 2538 in Oct.

F   Skinflats Est: 937 on 6 Jan, 847 on 10 Feb, 1128 on 9 Mar, 1007 on 14 Sep, 1506 on 26 Oct, 954 on 15 Nov and 1390 on 13 Dec. The ponds themselves held 50 birds 30 Mar, 18 Apr and 29 Jun and 300 on 13 Sep. Kinneil: ca. 350 on 26 Jan, 500 on 12 Feb, 80 on 3 Mar, 300 on 27 Jul, 805 on 29 Aug, 250 on 14 Sep, 100 on 23 Sep and 25 Nov.

C   6 Cambus Pools 23 Mar. 3 AOT Blackdevon Wetlands 13 May with 20 there 1 Nov. 14 Gartmorn 22 Nov.

S   17 Carron Valley Res 14 Jan with 20 there 12 Feb and 11 on 18 Nov. 70 flying along Forth past S Alloa Br 2 Feb. 11 Cambusmore/Gart 14 Jan. 5 Nether Carse 19 Feb. In breeding season: 2 nr N Third Reservoir 9 Apr; 2 Carron Valley Res

29 Apr and 1 there 18 Jun; 2-4 L Mahaick 8 May; 3 Gart GP 11 May and 2 Blairdrummond 16 May.

COMMON GREENSHANK *Tringa nebularia* (w, p)

WeBS estuary peaks were 4 in Jan and 11 in Sep.

F Present at Skinflats all year, except May. Max early in the year: 2 Jan, 3 Feb, 4 Mar, 4 Apr (RS, MVB, AB, GFB). A good autumn passage started with 2 on 25 Jun, increasing to 7 on 7 Jul, then 3 on 22 Jul, 2 on 31 Jul, 1 on 1 Aug, 3 on 11 Aug, 5 on 13 Aug, 8 on 16 Aug, increasing to 11 on 22 and 25 Aug, 10 on 29 Aug and 2 Sep, 7 on 7 and 9 Sep, 9 on 14 and 15 Sep, 7 on 18 Sep, 3 on 22 and 23 Sep and 3 Oct, 6 on 14 Oct and 4 on 28 Oct (AB, RDZ, CT, GFB, GO, GG, MVB, RS, DOE). Up to 5 birds (same as above ?) overwintered, being present on 15, 16, 22, 23, 24 Nov and 26 Dec (MVB, GO, BRG, AB, RS). At Kinneil all year, except June. A single overwintered being seen repeatedly 6 Jan to 3 Apr (DT, BRG, CJP, ACC, DM, GFB). There was a small spring passage with 1 bird 12 Apr, 2 birds 17 and 18 Apr, 3 on 28 Apr and singles 4 to 6 May (GFB, GO, AET, DT). Another good autumn passage started with 1 on 2, 5, 10, 17 and 18 Jul, then 2 on 23 Jul, 4 on 24 and 27 Jul, 2 on 1 Aug, 3 on 8 Aug, 4 on 13 Aug, 2 on 16, 22 and 31 Aug, 3 on 6 Sep, 12 on 18 Sep, 4 on 24 Sep, singles on 3, 11 and 12 Oct and 2 on 12 Oct (RS, BRG, DT, GO, ACC, AB, GFB, GO, EH). Up to 2 birds overwintered being seen on several dates from 11 Nov to 28 Dec (DT, RS, GO, AB, CT). Elsewhere 1 flew over Liddle Drive, Bo'ness 18 Nov (RE, RS)

C Singles Blackdevon Wetlands 18 Mar and Cambus Pools 23 Mar (CJH, ACC).

S 3 R Forth, E Frew-Gargunnock Br 27 Mar and 3 Nether Carse 27 Mar (ACR).

Autumn passage, area summary (minimum number/half month)							
Jul		Aug		Sep		Oct	
6	7	12	12	13	19	8	4

GREEN SANDPIPER *Tringa ochropus* (w, p)

This species now occurs as a wintering bird in small numbers as well as a passage migrant.

F As in the winter of 2006/07 2-3 birds overwintered with 2 on the R Carron, Carronbridge-Langlees stretch on 12 Jan and 9 Mar and 1 at Gilston Park, Polmont 7 and 8 Feb (AB, RS, GO). The only spring passage birds were 3 Kinneil 28 Apr (AET). A poor autumn passage saw singles at Kinneil 14 and 28 Aug and at Gilston on 14 and 15 Aug (DT, RS, DG, GO). An overwintering bird (same as early in year ?) was seen on the R Carron, M876-Larbert stretch 14 Sep, 26 Oct, 16 Nov and 14 Dec (MA).

S Singles Blairdrummond at L Daira 3 Feb and at unspecified location there 19 Apr (GEL, DOE). Singles Blairdummond at Quarry Loch 24 Nov and Coustry Pond there 18 Dec (NB). Are all of these the same bird ?

COMMON SANDPIPER *Tringa hypoleucos* (B)

F Kinneil: 1 on 14 Apr rising to 2 on 17 and 18 Apr. 4 on 2 Aug and 5 on 6 Sep. Skinflats: 1 on 5 and 12 May and 2 on 7 Jul.

C One Cambus Pools 20 Apr.

S One Gart/Cambusmore GP, Callander 15 Apr with 2 there 30 Apr, 4 on 11 May and 1 on 28 Jul. Singles L Ard 16 Apr and Airthrey L 21 Apr. 4 Carron Valley Res 29 Apr. 2 Arivurichardich Res, nr Callander 2 May. 1 Carse of Lecropt 3 May. 2 Cocksburn Res 7 May. 3 L Dochart 21 Jun. 2 Braeleny, BoD 30 Jun.

*SPOTTED SANDPIPER *Actitis macularia*

F The overwintering bird from 2007 continued its stay at the R Avon mouth, Kinneil, being repeatedly seen Jan to Mar and last seen on 14 Apr (CJP, RS, GO, JTMT, AB, DT, CT, AET, MMcG, BRG).

RUDDY TURNSTONE *Arenaria interpres* (W)
    WeBS estuary peaks were 6 in Jan and 5 in Nov.
C   One Kennetpans 13 Dec.
F   Five Carron mouth, Skinflats 6 Jan with 1 there 10 Feb (MVB). 1 Kinneil 6 Jan
    and 27 Jul, 2 there 1 Aug and 5 on 14 Nov (JRC, GO, AB). 3 Bo'ness 14 Sep, 1 on
    27 Oct and 3 on 13 Dec (JRC).
*ARCTIC SKUA *Stercorarius parasiticus* (p)
F   Kinneil: 2 on 10 Jul, 1 on 23 Jul, 5 on 6 Sep and 1 on 24 Sep (DT).
*BLACK-LEGGED KITTIWAKE *Rissa tridactyla* (P, w)
F   Thirty > W at Kinneil 5 Apr (GFB). 50 Kinneil 6 Sep (DT).
*MEDITERRANEAN GULL *Larus melanocephalus*
F   Ad Kinneil 10 Feb, and first winter 25 Oct (BRG, GO). Ad Skinflats 27 Jul and 23
    Nov (GO, BRG). These are the 13-14th and 16-17[h] records for the recording area.
S   One second summer bird Blairdrummond Safari Park 25 May (CM). 15th record
    for recording area.
*LITTLE GULL *Larus minutus*
F   Skinflats: 2 on 4 May; 3 first summer birds on 11 Jun (GO, AB). Kinneil: 1 ad on
    31 Jul; and 13, 17, 23 Aug (GFB, GO, DH). 17 ads >W at Kinneil 17 Sep (DMB).
BLACK-HEADED GULL *Larus ridibundus* (B,W)
    Inland WeBS counts: 1058in Jan, 722 in Feb, 933 in Mar, 449 in Sep, 969 in Oct,
    1360 in Nov, 794 in Dec.
    Forth Est (WeBS): 1272 in Jan, 1423 in Feb, 279 in Mar, 1341 in Sep, 597 in Oct,
    1693 in Nov, 944 in Dec.
F   Max counts: 428 Kinneil 6 Jan and 415 there 14 Sep.
C   Max counts: 640 Blackdevon Wetlands 6 Feb; 250 Gartmorn Dam 12 Feb; 1650 S
    Alloa 15 Nov.
S   Breeding: c200 Carron Valley Res incl 37+ juvs counted 23 Jun.
*RING-BILLED GULL *Larus delawarensis*
F   Returning ad at Kinneil from 2007 to 17 Feb and from 14 Aug to 25 Nov (RS, DT,
    GO *et al.*). This record is pending with SBRC.
MEW GULL (COMMON GULL) *Larus canus* (B,W)
    Inland WeBS counts: 215 in Jan, 287 in Feb, 424 in Mar, 599 in Sep, 369 in Oct,
    304 in Nov, 331 in Dec.
    Forth Est (WeBS): 100 in Jan, 201 in Feb, 124 in Mar, 21 in Sep, 77 in Oct, 110 in
    Nov, 64 in Dec.
F   Max counts: 364 Skinflats 19 Sep. 60 Kinneil 12 Feb with 100 there on 25 Nov. 79
    Bo'ness 14 Nov.
C   Max count: 75 Cambus 10 Feb.
S   Breeding: 6 ON Cambusmore 20 May. Max counts: 2029 King's Park, Stirling 2
    Jan; 350 Thornhill Carse 9 Mar.
LESSER BLACK-BACKED GULL *Larus fuscus* (b, S)
    Inland WeBS counts: 0 in Jan, 2 in Feb, 92 in Mar, 59 in Sep, 83 in Oct, 11 in Nov,
    3 in Dec.
    Forth Est (WeBS): 13 in Feb, 53 in Mar, 40 in Sep, 9 in Oct, 6 in Nov.
F   Max counts: 157 Skinflats 8 Mar; 52 Little Denny Res 14 Oct.
C   Max count: 40 Cambus 9 Mar. 13 Blackdevon Wetlands 11 Mar.
S   Max counts: 64 Lake of Menteith 11 Mar; 204 Thornhill Carse 4 Sep; 30 Airthrey
    Loch 22 Oct.
HERRING GULL *Larus argentatus* (b, W)
    Inland WeBS counts: 173 in Jan, 173 in Feb, 100 in Mar, 42 in Sep, 172 in Oct, 93
    in Nov, 97in Dec.
    Forth Est (WeBS): 24 in Jan, 249 in Feb, 178 in Mar, 574 in Sep, 60 in Oct, 70 in

Nov, 325 in Dec.
F   Max count: 400 Kinneil 28 Jun.
C   Max count: 208 S Alloa 14 Sep.

*ICELAND GULL *Larus glaucoides*
F   Ad Avondale Landfill, Polmont 13 Dec (CJP).

GREAT BLACK-BACKED GULL *Larus marinus* (S,W)
      Inland WeBS counts: 10 in Jan, 5 in Feb, 4 in Mar, 4 in Sep, 2 in Oct, 5 in Nov, 7 in Dec.
      Forth Est (WeBS): 8 in Jan, 11 in Feb, 32 in Mar, 7 in Sep, 2 in Oct, 9 in Nov, 7 in Dec.
F   Max count: 72 Kinneil 25 Aug.
C   Max count: 17 Cambus 9 Mar.
S   Nine Fallin 20 Jan. 1 R Forth, E Frew 28 Oct.

SANDWICH TERN *Sterna sandvicensis* (P)
      WeBS Est peak: 104 in Sep.
F   Kinneil: 2 on 3 Jul; 2 on 17 Aug; 2 on 14 Sep; 5 on 5 Oct. Skinflats: 3 on 31 Jul; 24 on 2 Sep; 12 on 13 Sep; 24 on 14 Sep; 2 on 18 Sep; 15 on 23 Sep. 65 Bo'ness 14 Sep. Blackness: 6 on 12 Oct and 14 on 13 Oct.

COMMON TERN *Sterna hirundo* (B)
F   First: 3 at Skinflats 4 May (GO), and 25 on 11 May. 1 Kincardine Br 18 May. Skinflats: up to 14 on 12 Jun. 1 Kinneil 17 Aug. 1 Kincardine Br 14 Sep.

ARCTIC TERN *Sterna paradisaea*
F   One Kinneil 28 Jun (ACC). This is the 16th record fro the recordimng area since 1974.

FERAL PIGEON *Columba livia* (B,W)
F   200 Kinneil 25 Nov.

STOCK PIGEON *Columba oenas* (B, W)
F   Two Kinneil 5 Jul. 9 Skinflats 6 Jul. 1 Parkhill, Polmont 8 Aug.
C   Two Woodland Park & Drove Rd, Alva 7 Jan. 1 Cambus Pools 20 Apr. 2 Blackdevon Wetlands 8 Jul and 1 Aug.
S   15 Keir Estate, BoA 3 Apr. 2 Arnprior 7 Apr.

COMMON WOOD PIGEON *Columba palumbus* (B, W)
      BBS: recorded at 3.8 b/lkm
F   200 Skinflats 13 Sep.
S   One singing BoA 6 to 29 Jan and 7 to 18 Feb where fledged juv 10 Apr. 80 Cambuskenneth 4 Jul with 150 there 17 Aug and 80 on 5 Sep.

EURASIAN COLLARED DOVE *Streptopelia decaocto* (B, W)
      Greatly under-reported. No significant records were received this year

COMMON CUCKOO *Cuculus canorus* (B)
      Arrival in Apr: Easter Poldar, Flanders Moss 25th was same date as in 2007 and 4 days later than in both 2005 and 2006 but with the next birds several days later than in 2007, i.e. in May where birds at Low Botaurnie, G Lochay 3rd; Ben Ledi 5th; Sheriffmuir 6th (2 birds); Braeleny, BoA 7th; Argaty, BoD 8th; Ruskie 10th, Carron Valley 10th (2 birds) and 2 at Gleann Dubh 11th.
F   Two California 7 Jun.
S   In late May: singles at Upper Lanrick, Callander 17th; Cromlix Moor 23rd; Brig o'Turk 24th; 2 Silver Strand, Loch Katrine 24th; Falls of Leny, Callander 25th. In June: singles Cobleland, Aberfoyle 7th; Gleann Dubh 8th; Cocksburn Res 11th and 3 at Sheriffmuir 20th.

BARN OWL *Tyto alba* (b, w)
      The increasing number of reports from a wider area, suggesting that the species is spreading.

F　　Singles Champany 1 Jan, Inchyra 22 Apr and Darnrig Moss former opencast coal site 16 Jun (RS, RDZ).

C　　One nr. Dollarbeg 1 Jan and 20 Nov. 1 dead on B9140 west of Fishcross 21 Mar. 1 Muirside Roundabout, Tullibody 2 Apr and Dumyat View Roundabout, Tullibody 12 Dec. 1 dead on A977 at Castlebridge Business Park, Forestmill 29 Oct (AET, JTMT, DAC)

S　　L Ard: singles Bad Dearg 9 Jan, Dun Dhamh 15 Jan, High Stiles Road 16 Jan, L Ard Forest 31 Jan with 2 Gleann Dubh 10 Mar and 1 there on 11 Mar. L Katrine: singles Rubha na Moine 21 Jan and Glengyle 31 Jan (ABu). BoD: 1 Dalbrack 3 Feb, 1 Argaty 12 Feb with 2 prs there 2 Jun, pr Kilbryde 26 Jun (DOE). Elsewhere singles Strathyre 6 Feb; Shaw of Touch, Gargunnock 18 Feb; Boquhan 20 Feb; Flanders Moss 16 Mar; catching prey below Stirling Castle at 2pm on 28 Apr; 1 dead on verge of Duthieston slip northbound A9 16 May; singles Barrowmeadow 16 Jun; Barbush Estate, Dunblane 1 Nov and Doune 25 Nov (Abu, DOE, ACR, CJM, MVB, NB).

TAWNY OWL　*Strix aluco*　(B, W)

F　　One Liddle Drive, Bo'ness 5 Jul.

C　　One calling Aberdona 18 Mar. 2 calling to each other Castlebridge Business Park, Forestmill 5 May.

S　　One calling Springwood Avenue, Stirling throughout year; singles Stronmacnair and Bad Dearg, L Ard 10 Jan; South Mid Frew, Kippen 29 Jan; Doune Rd, Dunblane 6 Feb and 5 Mar and Flanders Moss 18 Feb. Pr on eggs Cromlix 21 Mar. 4 prs Argaty, BoD 20 Apr. 1 at midday W of Gargunnock 21 May. Singles Cairnoch Hill, Carron Valley 24 May; Newton Crescent, Dunblane 28 Jul; Low Botaurnie, G Lochay 29 Jul; A91 at Springkerse Retail Park 1 Nov and Stirling 20 Dec.

LONG-EARED OWL　*Asio otus*　(b, w)

F　　Bird at Skinflats in former breeding location but no sign of breeding this year 4 May (AB).

S　　One heard L Mahaick 8 Jun. 1 Drumloist, BoD 14 Jun. 1 Burnside, Blairdrummond Moss 31 Oct (DOE, DI).

SHORT-EARED OWL　*Asio flammeus*　(b, W)

　　For this rather local breeder, a more systematic survey of known breeding areas and potential breeding sites would be of value.

F　　One Darnrig Moss 27 Mar. One seen most of Jun and found dead in Aug at Strathavon Fm, Slamannan (TF). 1 Falkirk Stadium injured by electric cables 27 Oct, died two days later (MW). 2 Kinneil 21 and 22 Nov with 1 there 30 Nov (RS, GO).

C　　Two Blackdevon Wetlands and 1 there 21 Nov. 1 Tullibody Inch 17 Sep (CJH, DOE, DMB).

S　　Two G Finglas 21 Jan. 1 at Culligart, Loch Katrine 27 Mar. 1 Touchadam Muir 14 May. 2 Braeleny, Callendar 30 June and 1 Bochastle, Callendar 6 Jul (RR, Abu, DT, DOE).

COMMON SWIFT　*Apus apus*　(B)

　　Spring arrival: 5 BoA 27 Apr were 1 day earlier than in 2007, 4 days earlier than in 2006 and 2 days earlier than in 2005. This was followed by 1 Carron Valley Res and 2 Dunblane 29 Apr, 5 Doune Castle 3 May, 3 Stirling and 1 Alva Glen 4 May, 2 BoA 5 May and 3 Alloa 6 May. The first larger flock was 25 in Callander on 24 May.

　　Autumn departure in Aug: 22 Doune 4th, 6 Queen Elizabeth Forest Park 3rd, 1 BoA 4th, 3 Carse of Lecropt 10th, 1 Coneyhill, BoA 13th, 2 Stirling 16th and 1 Carronshore 30th, which was 20 days later than in 2006, 2 days later than in 2006 and 11 days later than in 2005.

C   50 Gartmorn Dam 7 Jul.

S   Flock of between 20 and 37 birds BoA on various dates in July.

COMMON KINGFISHER *Alcedo atthis* (b, w)

F   Kinneil: singles 2, 4 and 8 Jan, 13 Aug (imm), 14 Sep, 11 and 12 Oct, 18 and 30 Nov. R Carron: 2 M876-Larbert 9 Mar, singles Larbert-Carron Br stretch 13 Jan and 10 Mar, Carron Br-Carron House 10 Feb, 14 Sep and 10 Oct, Langlees 10 Feb and 14 Sep and Carron Works 26 Oct. Skinflats: singles 2, 3 and 19 Sep and at Muirdyke Burn there 10 Oct. Elsewhere West Mains Industrial Estate Pond 15 Sep.

C   R Devon: 1 on B934 to Crook of Devon stretch 21 Sep with 2 there 18 Nov and 1 on 9 Dec, singles at Dollar 28 Nov, Dollar-Tillicoultry 19 Mar, 23 Sep and 26 Nov, Tillicoultry-Alva 14 Sep and 10 Oct. Elsewhere 1 at Cambus Pools 21 Nov.

S   Airthrey L: singles 11, 16, 21 Jan, 6 and 13 Feb, 25 Mar and 25 Oct. R Forth: singles Ladylands-Br of Frew 23 Sep, E Frew-Gargunnock Br 27 Mar, Teith-Allan confluences 15 Mar and 16 Nov (2), Allan-Stirling Br 30 Nov, Cambus-Fallin 21 Nov and 28 Dec (2). Elsewhere singles Nether Carse 27 Mar; Gart GP, Callendar 4 Apr and nearby on Keltie Water 19 Sep; Polmaise lagoons 26 Jun; Doune 9 Jul; Gartmore, Aberfoyle 4 Sep; The Meadows, Callander 15 Sep; Blairdrummond 25 Oct and 1 Nov; R. Teith, Doune Br-W Row 6 Dec (2) and Ashfield 15 Dec.

GREEN WOODPECKER *Picus viridis* (B, W)

      More records away from SE needed to establish true status.

F   Single Plean CP 15 Apr and 16 Jul.

C   Singles Alva Woodland Park and Drove Road 7 Jan and Alva Glen 16 Mar. 1 old railway E of Clackmannan 2 May. 1 above Menstrie 8 Oct.

S   One calling Argaty, BoD 13 Jan. 2 calling Crinigart Woods, Gartartan 11 Mar. 3 Blairdrummond 16 and 28 Apr. Singles Lundie, BoD 19 Apr; Doune Lodge 26 Apr; David Marshall Lodge 5 May; Airthrey L 17 May and 24 Jun; F and juv by Dumyat 24 Jul. 1 Dunblane 31 Aug and juv there Ochlochy Rd 1 Sep. 2 above BoA 23 Sep. Singles E of Blairlogie 6 Oct and Kilbryde, BoD 26 Oct.

GREAT SPOTTED WOODPECKER *Dendrocopus major* (B, W)

F   Singles Kinneil 4 Jan; Langlees woodland regeneration 12 Jan; Dunmore Woods 6 Mar; Denny 12 May. At least 2 prs Plean CP with Y at nest hole 6 Jun. Singles Wallacestone 16 Jun; Skinflats 19 and 30 Aug, 22 Sep and 28 Dec; Drumbowie Res, Denny 14 Oct; St Helen's Loch, Bonnybridge 14 Oct; Airth Castle 29 Oct and Grangemouth garden 6 Nov.

C   Singles Kennetpans 6 Jan (M); old railway E of Clackmannan 7 Jan with ad and juv there 16 Jun and single on 21 Oct; around Gartmorn 12 and 20 Jan and 13 May. Pr N of Cambus 8 Apr with single there 3 Nov. Along R Devon, Alva-Menstrie stretch 11 Apr, 15 Jun (2) and 27 Jul. Singles at Alva Glen 4 May; Blackgrange 27 Oct; N of Tullibody 15 and 18 Nov and 22 Dec.

S   Singles Flanders Moss 6 Jan and 2 at East Poldar there 25 Apr ; Argaty, BoD 13 Jan; Airthrey L 29 Jan; Castlebridge Business Park, Forestmill 6 and 11 Feb; Carron Valley Res 2 Feb, 18 Nov and 20 Dec, 29 Apr and 18 Jun; Blairdrummond Moss 14 Feb; drumming Port of Menteith 11 Mar; David Marshall Lodge area 13 Apr; Blairdrummond caravan park 16 Apr; Falls of Leny, Callander 25 May; Dunblane 14 Jun; Gallow Hill, BoA 22 Jun (M); Clash, Callander 24 Jun; Stronachlachar 1 Nov; L Lubnaig 2 Nov;

SKY LARK *Alauda arvensis* (B, W)

      BBS: recorded at 1.5 b/lkm.

F   Three singing Skinflats 18 Apr with 30 there 22 Sep and 15 on 2 Oct.

S   Ten Nether Carse 31 Jan. 10 Drip Moss 4 Mar. 121 Litleward, Thornhill Carse with 40 there 7 Apr.

SAND MARTIN *Riparia riparia* (B)

       Arrival: 4 Doune 30 Mar were 11 days later than in 2007, 10 days later than in 2006 and 13 days later than in 2005. This was followed by 2 BoA and 1 Lake of Menteith 1 Apr; 1 E of Tillicoultry 2 Apr; 10$^+$ Gart GP, Callander 4 Apr; 2 Carron Valley 5 Apr; 50 Gartmorn 5 Apr, 300$^+$ there 6 Apr but none 9 Apr; 25 Airthrey L 8 Apr and 30 there 18 Apr. No departure dates were received this year.

C   40 Old Stirling R, Tullibody 13 May. 30 Gartmorn 17 Jun but no sign of having used artificial nest bank there.

S   15 L Watston 16 Apr with 80 there 18 Apr. 90 Blairdrummond caravan park 16 Apr. 30 Callander 10 May. Ca. 60 active nest holes Cambusmore GP 29 Jun. 30 Gart 28 Jul.

BARN SWALLOW *Hirundo rustica* (B)

       BBS: recorded at 2.8 b/lkm.

       Spring arrival in Apr: 1 Gart GP 6 Apr was 31 days later than in 2007, 6 days later than in 2006 and 3 days later than in 2005. This was followed by 1 Airthrey L 8th; nr N Third Res and Argaty, BoA 9th; 1 Skinflats 10th; 1 Blairdrummond 13th. Autumn departure: 3 Kinneil 28 Sep; 1 Thornhill 30 Sep; 6 Old railway, E of Clackmannan 21 Oct; 6 Carron Dam 28 Oct and 2 Blackness 30 Oct, which was 25 days later than in 2007, 14 days later than in 2006 and 3 days earlier than in 2005.

F   42 Skinflats 11 May with 550 there 12 Sep and 40 on 13 Sep.

C   25 Blackgrange14 Sep.

S   33 L Coulter 24 Apr. 40 Glenhead 24 Jul. 80 Queen Elizabeth Park, Aberfoyle 30 Aug.

HOUSE MARTIN *Delichon urbica* (B)

       Arrival in Apr: 6 Blairdrummond caravan park 16th was 7 days later than in 2007, 2 days later than in 2006 and 9 days later than in 2005. This was followed by 15 Kippenross House, Dunblane 21st; 1 Carronshore 25th; 3 Cambus and 4 Kinbuck 26th.

       Departure: singles Airthrey L 21 Sep and Viewforth, Stirling 1 Oct, which was 20 days later than in 2007, on the same date as in 2006 and 10 days later than in 2005.

F   Six$^+$ nests with Y Bryce Avenue, Carron in Jul.

C   One nest Coalsnaughton centre 12 May.

S   21 Falls of Leny, Callander 25 May. 20 Dunblane 6 Jul. 25 Queen Elizabeth Park, Aberfoyle 3 Aug. Ca. 30 BoA 28 Aug. 5 nests Gatincaber Steadings 4 Sep.

TREE PIPIT *Anthus trivialis* (B)

       Arrival: 1 Argaty, BoD and 3 singing Dumyat, Stirling 27 Apr were 14 days later than in 2007, 10 days later than in 2006 and 15 days later than in 2005. Then none until 1 Cromlix 4 May and 2 Gartmorn 7 May. No departure dates were received this year.

C   One Gartmorn Dam 17 Jun.

S   In breeding season: 2 Brae of Boquhapple, Thornhill 17 May; 2 Loch Doon Forest Drive, Loch Ard Forest 20 May; 1 Brig o'Turk and 5 Letter, L of Katrine 24 May; 1 Falls of Leny, Callander 25 May; ca. 15 AOT Coille Coire Chuilc, Tyndrum 12 Jun; 1 L Dochart 21 Jun and 1 singing G Lochay 27 Jun.

MEADOW PIPIT *Anthus pratensis* (B, W)

       BBS: recorded at 4.1 b/lkm. Continues to be scarce mid-winter.

C   Two Blackdevon Wetlands 24 Jan. 30 Blackgrange 27 Oct.

S   18 Craigton Farm, Kinbuck 12 Jan. 30 Blairdrummond Moss 14 Feb. 35 Lower Auchinlay, Dunblane 30 Mar. 72 Gart GP 6 Apr. 100 Littleward, Thornhill Carse 7 Apr. 150 nr Inn, Sheriffmuir 23 Aug.

ROCK PIPIT *Anthus petrosus* (w)
C   One Tullibody Inch 9 Feb (DMB).

GREY WAGTAIL *Motacilla cinerea* (B, w)
F   R Carron: 2 M876-Larbert 16 Nov and 14 Dec; 3 Larbert-Carron Br 13 Jan with 1 there 12 Feb; 2 Carron Bridge-Carron House 12 Jan with 1 there 12 Feb; 2 Carron House-A905 12 Jan, 9 Feb, 1 on 9 Mar, pr on 11 Jun and pr on 26 Oct. Elsewhere Millhall Res, Polmont 9 Feb. 2 Kinneil 28 Nov.

C   R Devon: 3 Tillicoultry-Alva 12 Jan with pr there 2 Apr and 1 on 15 Nov; pr Alva-Menstrie 24 Mar and 2 Apr and 1 on 27 Sep. Cambus: 3 on 23 Mar with pr there 4 Aug and 1 on 3 Nov. Elsewhere 4 Alva Glen 16 Mar; 1 Gartmorn and 2 to E of site 6 Apr. Old railway, E of Clackmannan 21 Oct. 2 Tullibody Inch 31 Oct. 1 Kersiepow 6 Nov.

S   Allan Water: 1 Ashfield-Dunblane 12 Jan with 2 there 14 Dec; 4 Dunblane 10 Jun with pr there 8 Nov; 1 N of BoA 27 Oct. Singles R. Teith, Wester Row-Forth confluence 10 Feb; Cocksburn Res 3 Apr; collecting food Coneyhill, BoA 19 May; Airthrey L 20 May. Pr E of Kippen 21 May. Singles Lossburn Reservoir 23 Jul; Logie Church 27 Oct; Malling Lake of Menteith 12 Nov; R Forth, Fallin-Cambus stretch 21 Nov; The Meadows, Callendar 15 Dec and Springwood Avenue, Stirling 5, 6 and 12 Oct and 21 and 22 Dec.

PIED WAGTAIL *Motacilla alba* (B, w)
Fewer records in both the first and second winter seasons. 3 Jan records (9 in 2007, 3 in 2006 and 4 in 2005): 1 Flanders Moss 6 Jan; 1 Blackdevon Wetlands 9 Jan with 2 there 30 Jan. 3 Feb records (11 in 2007, 6 in 2006 and 1 in 2005): 1 on Forth, S of Cambus and 2 W of Alloa 2 Feb; 36 Stonehouse Fm, Skinflats 10 Feb. No November records (6 in 2005, 2006 and 2007) and 2 December records (7 in 2005, 2006 and 2007): 1 by Forth nr Alloa 6 Dec; roost at Stirling railway station 16 Dec.

F   Skinflats: 46 on 12 Feb; 6 on 30 Mar. White Wagtails (*M.a.alba*): 8 Skinflats 18 Apr and 11 there 28 Apr.

BOHEMIAN WAXWING *Bombycilla garrulus* (w)
Following the large invasion in 2004, this autumn saw another, albeit not quite as large, invasion in the UK. Unlike in 2004 the berry crop (especially Rowan and Whitebeam) was generally poor and birds appeared to move to southern Britain comparatively quickly. Although total flock sizes are very difficult to establish in any one location, there is some evidence of this from well watched locations, such as Dunblane and Stirling.

F   75+ Falkirk 12 Nov with 50-60 there 18-19 Nov and 21 on 4 Dec. 36 Grangemouth 16 Nov with 22 there 21 Nov and 25 on 30 Nov. 120+ Larbert 18 Nov. Up to 22 Carron 27 Nov to 6 Dec. 21 Bo'ness 29 Nov. Ca. 50 Skinflats 4 Dec with 130+ there 8 Dec.

C   Five South Alloa 1 Nov increased to 25 birds in the Alloa area by 15 Nov. Elsewhere 15 Alva 21 Alva; 120+ Gartmorn 2 Dec; 1 Cambus 12 Dec; 55 Clackmannan 25 Dec and up to 50 Tullibody 31 Dec.

S   Small flock from 2007 early in the year in Dunblane where 24 on 15 Jan and up to 26 birds between 14 and 23 Mar. 3 Bannockburn 18 Jan. The autumn influx began with 1 Fallin and 2 Strathyre 1 Nov. Dunblane: present on several days in Nov with 41+ on 2nd rising to 65 on 3rd, 80 on 20th, 200 on 21st, 220 on 22nd, with smaller flocks thereafter with 25 on 24th, 40 and 70 on 26th and 27th moving S though to be on passage, then in December 15 on 7th and 19 on 15th the largest flocks. Stirling: 1 on 4th Nov increased to ca. 20 on 8th, 80 on 9th, 200+ on 11th and 12th, then dropped to ca. 50 on 15th, 8 on 20th Nov, with 60+ on 8th, 20+ on 10th and at least 50 still on 29th and 30th Dec. BoA: 20 on 4th Nov with 40 on 7th, 32 on

19th, 60 on 4th Dec and ca. 30 on 25th. Elsewhere 5 Callander 5th Nov rising to 34 by 18th. 20 Doune 18th and 19th Nov and 13th Dec. 18 Carron Valley Res 18th Nov. 30 Fallin 30th Nov.

WHITE-THROATED DIPPER *Cinclus cinclus* (B, W)

F   R Carron: 1 Carron Glen 19 May; 2 Denny 18 Feb and 8 Sep; 1 Carron Works 10 Feb and 14 Sep. R Avon: 2 Polmonthill 3 Jan and 1 singing there 7 Jan.

C   R Devon: 7 on B934 to Crook of Devon stretch 27 Oct with 5 there 18 Nov and 6 there 9 Dec; 6 Dollar-Tillicoultry 18 Feb with 7 there 23 Sep, 9 on 26 Nov and 6 on 28 Nov; 6 Alva-Tillicoultry 12 Jan. Elsewhere 2 Cambus 3 Nov.

S   Allan Water: 4 Dunblane 19 Feb; 1 BoA 31 Jul. 2 Earlsburn, Carron Valley 10 Feb. 1 R Dochart at Ledcharrie 30 Dec.

WINTER WREN *Troglodytes troglodytes* (B, W)

Widespread and common. Under-recorded. BBS: recorded at 2.4 b/lkm.

C   12 Gartmorn 9 Apr with 16 there 7 May and 11 on 9 Jul. 20 Cambus 19 Sep.

S   10 Airthrey 16 May.

HEDGE ACCENTOR (DUNNOCK) *Accentor modularis* (B, W)

Widespread and common. Under-recorded.

S   Six Blairdrummond Moss 14 Feb. 6 Woodland Park and Drove Road, Alva 28 Feb. 7 King's Park, Stirling.

EUROPEAN ROBIN *Erithacus rubecula* (B,W)

Widespread and common. Under-recorded. BBS: recorded at 1.2 b/lkm.

F   Ad and 3 recently fledged Y Bryce Avenue, Carron 5 May.

C   20 Cambus Pools 19 Sep.

S   14 King's Park, Stirling 14 Feb.

COMMON REDSTART *Phoenicurus phoenicurus* (B)

Arrival: 1 Menteith 27 Apr was 5 days later than in 2007, 4 days later than in 2006 and 8 days later than in 2005. The next bird was not seen until 5 May at Buchany, BoD with 2 M there 10 May; 1 Kilbryde, BoD 9 May (KO, DOE).

S   Singles Upper Lanrick, Callander and Brae of Boquhapple, Thornhill 17 May; Brig o'Turk, Callander, Letter-L Katrine and Silver Strand-L Katrine, all 24 May; Cromlix 3 Jul (DK, NR, DP).

WHINCHAT *Saxicola rubetra* (B)

Spring arrival: 1 old railway, E of Clackmannan 2 May was 5 days later than in 2007 and 7-9 days later than during 2003-2006. This was followed by 1 G Artney path, Callander 5 May; pr Sheriffmuir 7 May with 2 prs there 8 May; 1 Ben Cleuch, 2 M Flanders Moss, 4 M Braeleny, Callander, and 2 M Carron Valley all on 10 May.

Autumn departure: 2 Skinflats 3 Sep with 1 there 13 Sep and 22 Sep. This was 45 days later than in 2007 and 21 days later than in 2006[1].

F   One Kinneil 3 Jul. Skinflats: 1 on 27 Jul, 4 on 28 Jul, 2 on 31 Jul and 1 Aug and 5 on 5 Aug.

S   Six Brig o'Turk 24 May. Pr and 1 Y Carron Valley Res 18 Jun. Pr and 3 Y Sheriffmuir 24 Jun with M there 9 Jul. 5 Low Botaurnie, G Lochay 29 Jul.

STONECHAT *Saxicola torquata* (b, w)

F   Kinneil: 13 on 26 Jan with 2 there 9 Feb, 1 on 5 Apr, M on 22 Aug, 2 on 28 and 29 Aug. Skinflats: F on 28 Feb, M on 30 Mar; ad feeding recently fledged Y 25 Jun, 2 on 7 Jul, 1 on 1 and 5 Aug, 2 on 12 Sep, 4 on 25 Sep, 1 on 2 Nov, pr on 18 Nov and 2 on 13 Dec. Elsewhere 1 California 7 Jun. 2 Carbrook Mains 27 Jun. 2 Kirkton Tip 27 Dec.

---

[1] The arrival and departure dates for some species may be affected by an increasing amount of data submitted, especially via Birdtrack.

C R Devon: 2 Alva-Menstrie 14 Jan with pr there 11 and 16 Apr and 2 on 9 Nov. Blackdevon Wetlands: pr 24 and 30 Jan with F there 27 Feb, M 14 Mar, 20 and 23 May, 2 prs on a few dates in May-Jul, F/juv 1 Aug, 1w M 21 Sep, 2 on 28 Oct and 1 Nov. 1 N of Tullibody 9 May and 16 Jun with pr there 22 Sep and 6 Oct, 2 prs 29 Oct and 1 pr 22 Dec. Elsewhere 1 Gartmorn 12 Feb. Pr Cambus 3 Nov. Pr S of Coalsnaughton 5 Nov.

S Three Flanders Moss 6 Jan with 2 prs there 10 May and 2 on 21 Oct. Pr Carse of Lecropt 12 Jan and 12 Oct with single at nearby Netherton Marsh 12 Jan. Carron Valley Res: 1 on 14 Jan with 2 there on 5 Apr, 1 on 29 Apr, 18 Jun, 18 Oct, 18 Nov and pr on 20 Dec. Polmaise Lagoons: pr on 16 Jan, 21 Feb, 31 Mar with pr and 4 Y on 22 May, juv on 26 Jun and 1 on 18 Dec. Pr Hillhead Pond, Thornhill 26 Jan and 19 Mar. Pr Lundie, BoD 17 Feb. 2 Cambuskenneth 26 Mar. 1 Dumyat, Stirling 27 Apr with pr there 27 Jul. Callander: 1 G Artney path 3 May; 4 M Braeleny 10 May, 1 Clash 24 Jun. Sheriffmuir: 1 on 6 May with 3 there 7 May, 3 on 20 Jun, 8 ad and 3 Y 23 Jun, pr at Lairhill on 23 Jul and 3 on 30 Nov. 5 Letter, L Katrine 24 May. Pr G Finglas 25 May. 2 Gartrenich, BoD 27 May and 8 Jul. 8 Low Botaurnie, G Lochay 29 Jul. 4 Queen Elizabeth Forest Park 3 Aug. 1 L Walton 14 Sep. 1 Kippen Muir 14 Sep. 2 prs Cromlix 21 Oct. 1 Dochart Haughs 15 Nov. 2 R Forth below Kippen 30 Nov.

NORTHERN WHEATEAR *Oenanthe oenanthe* (B)
> Spring arrival: pr N of Menstrie 6 Apr was 12 days later than in 2007, 3 days later than in 2006 and 16 days later than in 2005. The next birds (3) at Bows, BoD were not until 12th Apr with 3 M Kinneil 24th, 1 Cambus 26th, and 3 Dumyat, Stirling 27th.
> Autumn departure: 2 Skinflats 3 Sep and 1 Higgins Neuk 14 Sep, which was 25 days earlier than in 2007, 29 days later than in 2006 and 10 days later than in 2005.

F 4-6 Kinneil 28 Apr.
C F Blackdevon Wetlands 6 May.
S F at nest Sheriffmuir 24 Jun. Singles Cononish, Tyndrum 29 Jul and Lairhill, Sheriffmuir 23 Aug.

*RING OUZEL *Turdus torquatus* (b)
S One Ben Ledi 29 May (AW).

COMMON BLACKBIRD *Turdus merula* (B, W)
> BBS: recorded at 2.1 b/lkm.

C 20 Gartmorn 12 Nov with 25 there 8 Dec.
S 24 King's Park, Stirling 18 Mar, with 20 on 22 Apr and 25 on 19 May.

FIELDFARE *Turdus pilaris* (W)
> Spring departure: 50 Manor Loan, Tullibody 23 Apr, 220 Easter Buckieburn Carron Valley 24 Apr and 50 Nether Carse 27 Apr, which was 31 days later than in 2007, 17 days earlier than in 2006 and 2 days earlier than in 2005.
> Autumn arrival in October: 10 Ashfield 18th was 11 days later than in 2007, 9 days earlier than in 2006 and 2 days earlier than in 2005. This was followed by ca. 60 L Doine 22nd and 80 Dunmore Home Farm, Forth 30th.

F 92 Myot Hill, Denny 11 Jan. 80 Skinflats 15 Nov with 260 there 10 Dec and 240 on 13 Dec.
C 100 Gartmorn 13 Jan. 75 Cambus 21 Nov. 60 Blackgrange 22 Nov.
S 120 Lecropt 7 Jan with 500+ there 2 Nov. 100 Boquhan, Kippen 1 Nov. Ca. 60 Hutchison, Dunblane 10 Nov.

SONG THRUSH *Turdus philomelos* (B, W)
> Under-recorded.
> Fewer winter records than in 2007. Jan: N of Buchlyvie 6th, Ochiltree, Dunblane

12th and singing Coneyhill, BoA 27th. Feb: Dunblane 2nd and 23rd; BoA 12th and 14th; 9 King's Park, Stirling 14th and 5 Woodland Park and Drove Road, Alva and singing Skinflats 28th. Nov: 2 regular in Dunblane garden all month till year end. Dec: Alloa by R Forth 6th; N of Tillicoultry 22nd and E of Tillicoultry 24th.

C　6 Kinneil 30 Aug.

S　5 Ardeonaig, Loch Tay 14 Mar. 5 King's Park, Stirling 18 Mar.

REDWING　*Turdus iliacus* (W)

Spring departure: 31 King's Park, Stirling 14 Mar, 70 Pool of Muckhart 28 Mar and 5 Auchinlay, Dunblane 4 Apr, which was 29 days later than in 2007, 32 days later than in 2006 and 24 days later than in 2005.

Autumn arrival in Oct: 15 SW Stonehill, Dunblane 9th, which was 12 days later than in 2007, 3 days earlier than in 2006 and 1 day later than in 2005. Then 20 BoA 12th, 6 N of Tullibody 14th, ca. 50 Malling, Lake of Menteith, 10 Ashfield and 103 >SW Stockbridge, Dunblane all on 18th.

F　65 Union Canal 7 Dec. 240 Skinflats 10 Dec.

C　50 Gartmorn 2 Nov.

S　81 King's Park, Stirling and 100 Airthrey 22 Oct.

MISTLE THRUSH　*Turdus viscivorus*　(B, W)

Under-recorded. No noteworthy records received this year.

COMMON GRASSHOPPER WARBLER　*Locustella naevia* (b)

Spring arrival in Apr: 1 Blairdrummond 23rd was 2 days earlier than in 2007, 4 days earlier than in 2006 and on same day as in 2005. This was followed by 1 Carron Valley Res 29th where also 18th Jun.

C　One Cambus Pools 7 May was heard on several subsequent dates. 1 R Devon, Alva-Menstrie stretch 30 May.

S　Two Flanders Moss 2 May. 1 Carse of Lecropt 3 May and 5 Jul. 2 Blairdrummond 16 May. 1 Cornton caravan park, Stirling 3 Jun. 1 Aberfoyle 21 Jul.

SEDGE WARBLER　*Acrocephalus schoenobaenus* (B)

Spring arrival in Apr: 1 singing Skinflats 27th was 2 days later than in 2007, on same day as in 2006 and 4 days earlier than in 2005. Then 1 singing Kinneil 29th.

Autumn departure: singles Skinflats 19 Aug, 29 Aug and 22 Sep, which was 43 days later than in 2007, 39 days later than in 2006 and 16 days later than in 2005.

F　Eight singing Skinflats 4 May with 7 there 7 May.

C　Four Gartmorn and 6 Cambus 7 May. 11 R Devon, Alva- Menstrie stretch 9 May. In breeding season also recorded at Tullibody and Blackdevon Wetlands.

S　In breeding season at: Blairdrummond; Cromlix; Ruskie, Thornhill and Cambuskenneth.

BLACKCAP　*Sylvia atricapilla* (B)

Winter records: Stirling: F Springwood Avenue 1 Jan to 31 Mar and M Queen Street 13 Jan. F Tillicoultry garden 28 Nov.

Spring arrival: M Springwood Avenue, Stirling 5 Mar; single Cocksburn Res 22 Mar and pr Alexander Drive, BoA 5 Apr could have been early migrants or overwintering birds. 1 singing Kinneil Wood 19 Apr. M Lanrick, BoD 24 Apr. M singing Coneyhill, BoA 26 and 27 Apr. 3 Menteith and 1 Skinflats 27 Apr.

F　Five singing Plean CP 5 May. 3 singing Skinflats 6 May with 1 there 19 Aug and 4 Sep, 3 on 12 Sep and M on 16 Sep. 2 Kinneil 21 and 24 Sep.

S　Two Airthrey 7 May and 17 Sep. 1 L Dochart 21 Jun.

GARDEN WARBLER　*Sylvia borin* (B)

Spring arrival: 1 Cocksburn 23 Apr was 5 days earlier than in 2007, 11 days earlier than in 2006 and 9 days earlier than in 2005.

Autumn departure: 1 Skinflats 4 Sep was 23 days later than in 2006 and 6 days later than in 2004.

F   Three Plean CP singing 8 May.

C   One old railway, E of Clackmannan 2 and 13 May. 3 Gartmorn 10 May and 9 Jul.

S   Singles Carse of Lecropt 3 May and Kinbuck Br 6 May. 2 singing Gartmore, R Teith 7 May. 1 Lanrick, BoD 8 May. 4 SE end L Katrine 24 May. 2 Kilmahog, Callander 25 May. Dunblane: 1 N of Cathedral 4 Jun and 2 at Allan Water 10 Jun.

COMMON WHITETHROAT *Sylvia communis* (B)

Spring arrival in Apr: 1 singing Skinflats 24th (2 there 26th) was 1 day later than in 2007, 2 days earlier than in 2006 and 6 days earlier than in 2005. Then singles Carronshore 25th and Dunmore 27th.

Autumn departure: 3 Ashfield 16 Aug, 2 Kinneil 29 Aug, 1 Skinflats 12 Sep, 1 Kinneil 13 and 24 Sep, which was 53 days later than in 2007, 32 days later than in 2006 and 19 days later than in 2005.

F   Five singing Skinflats 4 May. Elsewhere in breeding season at: Grangemouth garden, Kinneil and Chasefield, Denny.

C   Seven R Devon, Alva-Menstrie stretch 9 May. Elsewhere during breeding season at: old railway, E of Clackmannan, Gartmorn; old Stirling road path, Tullibody.

S   Five Kinbuck Br 5 May. In breeding season also in Dunblane; Doune and Cornton caravan park, Stirling.

WOOD WARBLER *Phylloscopus sibilatrix* (B)

Under-recorded.

Spring arrival: 1 singing Kippenrait Glen, BoA 30 Apr was 3 days later than in 2007, 1 day later than in 2006 and on the same day as in 2005. Then 1 Ben Ledi 5 May. 1 E of Gartmorn 10 and 13 May. 2 Braeleny, Callendar 10 May. 2 Brig o'Turk 17 May.

S   Loch Katrine: 3 Letter, 1 Silver Strand and 6 at SE end, all on 24 May. Callander: 2 Falls of Leny and 5 Kilmahog 25 May. 1 Lake of Menteith 26 May.

COMMON CHIFFCHAFF *Phylloscopus collybita* (B)

Winter record: singles Kinneil 4 Jan and Cambus 28 Nov.

Spring arrival: singles Union Canal Tunnel, Falkirk and Doune 30 Mar were 15 days later than in 2007, 1 day earlier than in 2006 and 6 days later than in 2005. Then 1 E of Clackmannnan 2 Apr. 1 BoA 3 Apr. 1 Drumloist, BoD and 3 Laighills to Ashfield, Dunblane 4 Apr. 1 Viewforth, Stirling 5 Apr. 1 Gartmorn 6 Apr. 2 N of Menstrie 7 Apr and 1 Skinflats 8 Apr.

Autumn departure: 1 Langlees, Carron 14 Sep and 1 singing N of Clackmannan 25 Sep, which was 11 days earlier than in 2007, 9 days earlier than in 2006 and 1 day earlier than in 2005.

F   Breeding season: 3 Plean CP. Singles Skinflats; Kinneil Wood and Callendar Park, Falkirk.

C   Breeding season: Tillicoultry.

S   Breeding season: BoA.

WILLOW WARBLER *Phylloscopus trochilus* (B)

Spring arrival in Apr: 1 singing Skinflats 8th was 3 days earlier than in 2007, 6 days earlier than in 2006 and 5 days later than in 2005. Then singles R Devon, Alva-Menstrie 11th, Blairdrummond 13th, Airthrey 14th, Gartmorn 15th after which widespread.

Autumn departure in Sep: 2 Skinflats 12th and 1 Blackgrange 14th, which was 21 days earlier than in 2007, 3 days earlier than in 2006 and 20 days earlier than in 2005.

F   Eight singing Skinflats 24 Apr. 8 singing Plean CP 8 May. 20[+] Skinflats 19 Aug. In breeding season also: Carronshore, Plean and Skinflats.

C   Fourteen Gartmorn 7 May with 12 there 17 Jun and 4 Aug. In breeding season also: Cambus and Alva.

S   Ten Airthrey 16 May. 14 Brae of Boquhapple 17 May. In breeding season also: Dunblane, Flanders Moss, Sheriffmuir, Stirling, Loch Rusky and Monachyle Glen.

GOLDCREST *Regulus regulus* (B, W)

Under-recorded. Again no notable records were received.

FIRECREST *Regulus ignicapilla*

F   One Polmonthill, Grangemouth 3 Jan (SP) was also seen 6, 7, 19 and 26 Jan (RS, GO, AB, CJP, SP). This is the first record for the recording area since systematic recording began in 1974.

SPOTTED FLYCATCHER *Muscicapa striata* (B)

Spring arrival in May: pr Doune Lodge, BoD 13th were 6 days earlier than in 2007, 4 days later than in 2006 and 1 day earlier than in 2005.

Autumn departure: 2 Skinflats 13 and 30 Aug. 2 Killin Marshes 8 Sep were 15 days later than in 2006.

F   One Strathavon Fm, Slamannan 17 Jun.

C   One Woodland Park & Drove Road, Alva 29 Jun.

S   Two at nest site W of Gargunnock 21 May. 1 Brig o'Turk 24 May. Prs Doune and Callander 28 May. 3 prs Stronachlachar 13 Jun. 1 Stockbridge, Dunblane 18 Jun. 1 Clash, Callander 24 Jun. 1 G Lochay, Killin 11 Jul. 1 feeding Y Inverlochlarig 13 Jul.

PIED FLYCATCHER *Ficedula hypoleuca* (b)

S   Two Brig o'Turk 24 May (DK).

LONG-TAILED TIT *Aegithalos caudatus* (B, W)

F   Eleven Skinflats 14 Oct. 17 Kinneil 30 Oct.

C   Nine Gartmorn 20 Jan with 12 there 12 Nov. 12 Craigknowe, Ochil Road, Alva 26 Jan.

S   Ten Old Stirling Br 3 Jan. 11 Barr Wood, Bannockburn 3 Feb. 15 Airthrey 17 Sep, 12 there 30 Oct and 15 on 24 Nov. 12 E of Blairlogie 6 Oct. 12 Doune Rd, Dunblane 25 Dec.

BLUE TIT *Cyanistes caeruleus* (B, W)

Under-recorded. BBS: recorded at 1.5 b/lkm.

S   22 King's Park, Stirling 18 Mar.

GREAT TIT *Parus major* (B, W)

Under-recorded.

C   Twenty-one Woodland Park and Drove Road, Alva 7 Jan with 10 there 14 Feb. 10 Gartmorn 12 Feb with 12 there 9 Apr and 10 on 17 Jun.

S   One singing Coneyhill, BoA 12 Feb. 10 Blairdrummond Moss 14 Feb. 18 BoA 22 Mar.

COAL TIT *Periparus ater* (B, W)

Widespread but under-recorded.

S   Six[+] Springwood Avenue, Stirling 1 to 30 Nov.

WOOD NUTHATCH *Sitta europaea*

S   One Blairdrummond caravan park 16 and 18 Apr (KS). 1 calling in woodland behind Blairlowan, Sheriffmuir Road, BoA (DMB) and what was probably the same bird on feeders by Mine Wood, BoA 5 Sep and 30 Nov (RSX). These are the 6th and 7th records of this species for our area since 1974 and continue the recent run since 1999.

EURASIAN TREECREEPER *Certhia familiaris* (B, W)

Under-recorded.

F   Three Plean CP, including 1 gathering insects 8 May.

S   Breeding season: 2 Airthrey 21 Apr.

EURASIAN JAY *Garrulus glandarius* (B, W)
F   One Airth 16 Jan. 1 Plean CP 8 May. 2 Chasefield, Denny 13 Aug. 2 Torwood 11 Dec.
C   One W of Forestmill 6 Apr with 2 at Forestmill 28 Apr. Singles Gartmorn 13 May, 5 and 12 Nov. Two old railway, E of Clackmannan 16 Jun with 5 there 21 Oct. 1 Castle Campbell, Dollar 24 Jul with 1 at Dollar 28 Nov.
S   Jan-Feb: Flanders Moss; Argaty, BoD; L Venachar; Baxter's Loan, Dunblane; Sommer's Lane, Blairdrummond; N of BoA; Brig o'Turk (2). Breeding season: 2 Blairdrummond caravan park 16 Apr. Singles Bonnybridge 23 Apr and Carron Valley Res 29 Apr. 2 Chartershall, Stirling 17 May with 1 there 6 Jul. Singles Cromlix Moor 23 May and E of Brig o'Turk 25 May. 2 L Voil 12 Jun. Singles Queen Elizabeth Forest Park 3 Aug and Dunblane 16 Aug. Oct-Dec: 7 L Doine. Singles Auchlyne, G Dochart and Blackwater Marshes, L Venachar. 2 Callandrade, Callander.

EURASIAN MAGPIE *Pica pica* (B, W)
     Continues to be very scarce NW of Dunblane. Abundant around Stirling but is not usually as frequent in the west; large groups now widespread in Falkirk
F   Five Chasefield, Denny 21 Jul and 13 Aug. 6 Kinneil 30 Aug. 30 Carronshore 19 Nov.
C   R Devon, Alva: 5 on 12 Jan with 8 there 9 Mar and 5 on 14 Sep. 12 Cambus 6 Jan with 36 there on 13 Jan.
S   Six Airthrey 11 Jan with 12 there 13 Feb were again low counts compared to past roost counts. 7 Bannockburn 20 Feb. 10 Bonnybridge 25 Sep. 5 King's Park, Stirling 22 Oct. 1 Callandrade, Callander 12 Dec.

EURASIAN JACKDAW *Corvus monedula* (B, W)
     Under-recorded. BBS: recorded at 2.4 b/lkm.
F   At least 3 prs with Y at ruin, Plean CP.
S   Stirling: 280 King's Park 2 Jan with 404 there 28 Oct. 60 Airthrey 4 Nov. 50 Nyadd Fm 9 Nov. 80 Barr Wood, Bannockburn 3 Feb. 110 Blairdrummond caravan park 16 Apr. 120 Cambuskenneth 17 Aug.

ROOK *Corvus frugilegus* (B, W)
     BBS: recorded at 4.2 b/lkm. Systematic counts of known rookeries (e.g. BoA, Gartmorn, Forth & Clyde Canal, Lake of Menteith, etc.) needed.
F   Rookeries: 14 nests at Westbourne Avenue, Falkirk 22 Mar; 32 nests at Lock 16, Union Canal, Camelon 22 Mar; 20 occupied nests at William Simpsons House, Plean.
C   Alloa W: 64 nests in railway poplars 22 Apr. 150 birds Blackgrange 22 Nov.
S   210 King's Park, Stirling 2 Jan. 178 Drip Moss 27 Feb. 126 Blairdrummond caravan park 16 Apr. 120 Blairdrummond Moss 30 Jun. 150 Airthrey 4 Nov.

CARRION CROW *Corvus corone* (B, W)
     BBS: recorded at 2.8 b/lkm.
F   Fifty Kinneil 23 Sep.
C   Alva: 30 River Devon at Alva 17 Feb, 5 Oct and 7 Dec. 30 Woodland Park and Drove Road 28 Feb and 3 Mar. 30 Blackgrange 14 Sep and 27 Oct with 40 there 22 Nov.
S   Forty-four L Watston 4 Jan.

HOODED CROW *Corvus cornix* (b, w)
F   Four Skinflats 24 Apr feeding on seeded field with 1 there 26 Apr.
S   One L Lubhair and 2 Croftchois, Dochart Haughs 16 Jan. Singles Rhuveag, L. Voil 12 Feb; Brig o'Turk 16 Feb; Tyndrum 12 Apr and 22 Jun and at Balquhidder 17 Apr. 5 Monachyle Glen 20 Apr. Singles Low Botaurnie, G Lochay 3 May and L Voil 7 May. G Dochart: 2 Ledcharrie 8 Sep and 12 Auchlyne 15 Nov.

COMMON RAVEN *Corvus corax* (B, W)

There were again a number of reports from south/southwest of the core Callander-Doune-Dunblane area but now possibly well established outside.

C   Two flying over Castlebridge Business Park, Forestmill 17 Jun. 1 Colsnaur Hill 24 Jun. 1 Menstrie Glen 15 Nov.

S   Core area: two Inverlochlarig 12 Jan. 4 Couligartan, Loch Ard 7 Feb. 1 Vale of Coustry 10 Feb. 9 L Mahaick 17 Mar. Singles incubating Drumloist, BoD 20 Mar; Argaty, BoD 21 Mar and Cromlix 21 Mar where 2 on 3 Jul and 17 Dec. 4 Low Botaurnie, G Lochay 3 May. 1 Gleann Dubh 11 May. 1 Falls of Leny, Callander 25 May. 2 Gleann Breac-nic 8 Jun. 2 David Marshall Lodge, Aberfoyle 4 Sep. 4 over Newton Crescent, Dunblane 5 Sep. 3 Kilbryde, BoD 26 Oct. 13 Doune Lodge, BoD roost 21 Nov. Outside of core area: 2 Cairnoch Hill, Carron Valley 19 Jan. 5 S L Coulter 9 Feb and 1 there 16 Feb. 3 Carron Valley Res 12 Feb. 1 Sheriffmuir 14 Feb with 3 there 6 May, 1 incubating 8 May and 1 on 20 Jun. 1 Dumyat, Stirling 27 Apr. 1 Whins of Milton, Stirling 6 Jul. 2 Malling, Lake of Menteith 4 Sep. 1 Flanders Moss 14 Sep. 2 Airthrey 30 Oct. 2 >W BoA 27 Nov. 2 R Forth, Kippen 30 Nov.

COMMON STARLING *Sturnus vulgaris* (B, W)

Greatly under-reported. BBS: recorded at 5.0 b/lkm.

F   500 Chasefield, Denny. 100 Bonnybridge 28 Oct.

C   100 Blackgrange 27 Oct with 65 there 22 Nov.

S   200 Carron Bridge, Carron Valley 16 Feb. 300 Glenhead 2 Mar with 100 there 18 Jun, 16 Jul and 8 Oct. During breeding season also reported from Bonnybridge and Thornhill.

HOUSE SPARROW *Passer domesticus* (B, W)

Under-recorded. BBS: recorded at 1.7 b/lkm.

F   Breeding season: 8 Kincardine Br 18 May. 30 Falkirk 20 May. 12 Chasefield, Denny 19 Jul. Non-breeding: 25 Langlees, Carron 26 Oct and 15 there 18 Nov.

C   Twenty Gartmorn Dam 23 Sep.

S   Breeding season: 6 Argaty Fm, BoD 18 Mar; 1 Glenhead 13 May and 6 Callander 24 May. Non-breeding: 20 Kinbuck 27 Jan with 30 there 6 Mar. 26 Blair-drummond Moss 14 Feb. 20 Nether Carse 19 Feb. 25 S Mid Frew, Kippen 21 Mar. Ca. 20 Broomridge, Stirling where absent for years 23 Nov. None Springwood Avenue, Stirling where common 10 years ago.

EURASIAN TREE SPARROW *Passer montanus* (B, W)

Only small flocks this year.

F   Newton Rd, Skinflats: small flocks of 1 to 14 birds in Feb, Apr, Jun and Nov. Elsewhere Skinflats 2 on 11 Jan; 1 to NW on 3 Mar; 8 on 21 Apr, 9 on 28 Jul, 6 on 13 Aug and 15 at ponds 13 Sep. 1 on sea wall, Kinneil 22 Aug.

C   Old railway, E of Clackmannan: 2 on feeders 7 Jan with 3 there 2 May and 4 on 16 Jun. 3 Kennetpans 18 May. 4 Gartmorn 12 Oct. 2 Blackgrange 27 Oct.

S   Kinbuck: 1 to 6 birds on several days Jan-Mar. Doune Rd, Dunblane: 1 to 4 birds on several days Jan, Feb, May- Jul and Sep. Blairdrummond: 1 to 4 birds on several days Feb and Apr-Jun. Carse of Lecropt: 1 on 5 Jul, ca. 30 on 13 Sep, 25 on 22 Nov and 13 on 14 Dec. Elsewhere: 1 Brig o'Turk 16 Feb. 9 Littleward, Thornhill Carse 9 Mar. 2 S Mid Frew, Kippen 21 Mar. 2 Carbrook Mains, Plean 8 May with 5 there 27 Jun. 3 BoA 22 May.

CHAFFINCH *Fringilla coelebs* (B, W)

BBS: recorded at 3.2 b/lkm.

S   One singing Coneyhill, BoA 12 Feb. Carse of Lecropt: 850 on 7 Jan with ca. 400 at Longleys 12 Jan. 185 Baxter's Loan, Dunblane 20 Jan with 140 at Stonehill Fm 22 Oct. 350 Westerton Fm, Doune 22 Jan. BoD: 200 Argaty 23 Jan with 470 there

28 Feb and 430 on 28 Oct. 120 Blairdrummond Moss 14 Feb.

BRAMBLING   *Fringilla montifringilla* (W)

S   Two Longleys, Carse of Lecropt 12 Jan. Singles Baxter's Loan, Dunblane 20 Jan and Rossburn Lane, Blairdrummond Moss 22 Jan. 2 Bows, BoD 3 Feb. 1 Ochiltree, Dunblane 20 Oct.

EUROPEAN GREENFINCH   *Carduelis chloris* (B, W)

Under-recorded.

F   Fifty roosting Strathavon Fm, Slamannan Nov-Dec.

S   Sixty Baxter's Loan, Dunblane 20 Jan. 20 Tyndrum 24 Jun.

EUROPEAN GOLDFINCH   *Carduelis carduelis* (B, W)

Again no significant flocks reported from the Doune-Dunblane area.

F   Skinflats: 40 on 31 Jul; 20 at Muirdyke Burn, Powfoulis 10 Oct; 110 on saltmarsh 28 Oct with 40 there 24 Nov and 110 on 10 Dec.

C   Ca. 50 Cambus 1 Sep. Ca. 12 Kersiepow, Alva 1 Sep. 120 Blackgrange 14 Sep.

S   Forty-five Baxter's Loan, Dunblane 20 Jan. 36 Little Denny Res 12 Sep. 40 Doune 14 Dec.

EURASIAN SISKIN   *Carduelis spinus* (B, W)

F   Twenty Polmonthill 7 Jan. 21 Falkirk 28 Feb. 15 in woodland regeneration Langlees, Carron 20 Nov.

S   Thirty Coneyhill, BoA 14 Jan. 45 Ochiltree, Dunblane 19 Jan. 70 Bigg Wood, Dunblane 27 Jan. 55 Scout Head, Gargunnock 17 Feb. 50 Tyndrum 22 Jun with 30 there 24 Jun. 120 Newton Crescent, Dunblane 12 Sep with 130 there 16 Sep.

COMMON LINNET   *Carduelis cannabina* (B, W)

No records from the Doune and Carse of Lecropt areas; only one small flock in the Dunblane area.

F   Sixty-five Skinflats 6 Jan with 25 there on saltmarsh 22 Sep and 120 on 10 Dec.

C   Twenty Gartmorn 20 Jan and 13 Mar. 25 Tullibody Inch 9 Feb. 56 N of Tullibody 28 Nov.

S   100+ in newly planted Willow coppice Netherton, S of Thornhill 6 Feb. 70 Stonehill Fm, Dunblane 13 Sep.

TWITE   *Carduelis flavirostris* (b, W)

F   Eighty Airth-Dunmore 9 Feb. 4 Strathavon Fm, Slamannan 27 Feb. 4 Kinneil 25 Nov. 45 on saltmarsh at Skinflats 10 Dec.

C   Eleven Longcarse, Alloa 13 Jan.2 Tullibody Inch 9 Feb. 8 old railway E of Clackmannan 21 Oct.

S   BoD: 10 Waterside 6 Jan; 60 Argaty 19 Jan; 12 Lerrocks 22 Jan with 90 there 28 Feb and 16 on 31 Mar; 2 Lundie 4 Apr; 4 Bows 12 Apr; 11 Argaty Fm 18 Apr and 1 Mid Lundie 1 Jul. Elsewhere 49 Dunblane 10 Jan. 100 Doune 27 Jan. Ca. 80 in newly planted willow coppice Netherton, S of Thornhill 10 Feb. 1 Balquhidder 14 Apr. 2 Braeleny, Callendar 10 May with 5 there 30 Jun. 1 Gleann Breac-nic 8 Jun. 3+ prs G Lochay 27 Jun. 4 prs with Y Inverlochlarig 13 Jul.

LESSER REDPOLL   *Carduelis cabaret* (b, W)

F   Thirteen Kinneil 4 Jan. Grangemouth garden: 15 on 20 Jan, 34 on 22 Jan and 21 on 7 Feb.

S   Forty-five Darn Walk, BoA 1 Jan. 15 Doune 23 Jan. 10 Ardchullarie, L Lubnaig 15 Feb. 30 Newton Crescent, Dunblane 16 Sep. 32 Carron Valley Res 18 Nov. 16 Argaty, BoD 2 Dec. Ones or twos during breeding season at Carron Valley Res, Balquhidder, Airthrey, Kinbuck and Brig o'Turk. 8 Letter, L Katrine 24 May. 10 Inverlochlarig 13 Jul.

COMMON CROSSBILL   *Loxia curvirostra* (b, W)

F   Three Kirkton tip 27 Dec.

S   BoD: 4 Doune Lodge 6 Jan; 6 Argaty 19 Jan; 7 Kilbryde 24 Jan and M Lerrocks

28 Feb. Carron Valley: 4 Cairnoch Hill 19 Jan; 10 Cringate Muir 10 Feb; 1 at reservoir 12 Feb with 2 there 15 Mar, 7 (incl juvs) 29 Apr and 5 on 11 Jun; 2 there in unspecified location on 16 Apr and 11 on 5 Apr. Elsewhere 10 L Ard Forest 19 Jan. 1 Sheriffmuir 14 Feb. 4 L Rusky 19 Feb. 2 Monachyle Glen 20 Apr. 20 Hutchinson L, Cromlix 5 May with 2 at Cromlix Moor 23 May. 40 Real Food Café, Tyndrum 25 May. 50 Hermitage Wood, BoA 28 Jun. 1 Blairdrummond 25 Oct. 2 flying over Springkerse, Stirling 1 Nov.

COMMON ROSEFINCH *Carpodacus erythrinus*
S   M on feeders at Real Food Café, Tyndrum 19 Jun to 14 Jul (BA, AET, JTMT, WT, BG, DMB, BRG). This is the fifth record for the recording area with previous records from 1997, 1998, 2002 and 2005.

COMMON BULLFINCH *Pyrrhula pyrrhula* (B, W)
C   Six old railway, E of Clackmannan 7 Jan with 8 there 21 Oct.
S   Five M, 1F throughout Jan Springwood Avenue, Stirling feeding on Sycamore seeds with 5M, 2F there 21 Feb feeding on *Forsythia* buds and Sycamore seeds. Three prs Flanders Moss, N of Buchlyvie 6 Jan. 6 Lerrocks, BoD 22 Jan. 6 Airthrey 26 Sep. 8 Harperstone, Sheriffmuir 1 Nov. 11 King's Park, Stirling 28 Nov. In breeding season: R Teith, Gartmore and Coneyhill, BoA where a juv seen food begging 9 Jul.

SNOW BUNTING *Plectrophenax nivalis* (W)
F   One Kinneil 22 Nov (GO).
S   Five Craigmore, Aberfoyle 2 Feb with 2 at Duke's Pass, Aberfoyle 3 Feb. 2 Earlsburn 9 Feb (AB, DOE, DB). 2 Ben Ledi 11 Oct. 1 flew over Blairdrummond 1 Nov. 2 L Ard 3 Nov (WR, CJP, DOE).

YELLOWHAMMER *Emberiza citrinella* (B, W)
F   Skinflats: 19 on 6 Jan with 8 there 11 Jan, 20 on 3 Mar, 12 on 9 Mar and 15 on 13 Sep.
C   Five Old Stirling Rd, Tullibody 13 May.
S   Ca. 30 Rossburn Lane, Blairdrummond 22 Jan and 27 Feb with 21 on the Moss 14 Feb. 25 Littleward, Thornhill Carse 9 Mar with 14 there 23 Mar. 24 S Mid Frew, Kippen 21 Mar.

REED BUNTING *Emberiza schoeniclus* (B, W)
F   Skinflats: 18 on 6 Jan; 30 Newton Rd 28 Feb; 5 at ponds 13 Sep; 15 on 18 Nov. 6 R Carron, B902-Carron House 14 Sep.
C   Six Gartmorn 20 Jan with 7 there 12 Feb, 6 on 23 Sep and 6 on 8 Dec. 6 Blackdevon Wetlands 12 Feb with 2M there 6 May and 6 birds on 1 Nov. 20 Blackgrange 27 Oct and 5 on 22 Nov.
S   Ca. 20 Rossburn Lane, Blairdrummond 22 Jan with 15$^+$ on 27 Feb and 17 on the Moss 14 Feb. 45 Littleward, Thornhill Carse 9 Mar with 5 there 23 Mar.

ESCAPED SPECIES

SWAN (CHINESE) GOOSE *Anser cygnoides*
S   Three Airthrey 26 Jan with singles there 6 Sep, 2, 14 and 28 Oct and 20 Nov (CJP, MIA). Probably the same bird(s) present since at least 2003. This therefore remains the first record of this species for our area since 1974.

BAR-HEADED GOOSE *Anser indicus*
       This is the second record of this species for our area.
F   One Blackness 14 Aug in flock of 310 Greylag Geese (DAC). Could be the same bird as at Thornhill Oct 2006.

WOOD DUCK *Aix sponsa*
       This is the fourth record of this species for our area. Although the male may be

the same bird as the long-staying Stirling bird last seen in Jan 2006, the female is a new bird.

F   Union Canal: pr near Falkirk Tunnel 4 Jan and 17 Feb; one at Greenbank 29 Mar; M Summerford-Glen village 14 Sep (RDZ, SM, CMO). These probably all relate to the same individual(s).

WHITE STORK *Ciconia ciconia*

This is the first record for our area of a bird that was clearly not wild.

S   One Blairdrummond 25 May to year end had a plastic ring (CJP).

BARBARY DOVE *Streptopelia roseogrisea* var. *risoria*

This is the first known record of this domesticated species for our area.

F   One Liddle Drive, Bo'ness 5 and 6 Jul (RS).

PIN-TAILED WHYDAH *Vidua macroura*

This is the first known record of this species for our area.

C   One Craigknowe, Ochil Road, Alva 13 Nov (PA).

BOOK REVIEW

Light on Dark Age Scotland

Vol. 1 and 2 of the **New Edinburgh History of Scotland**
Vol. 1 **From Caledonia to Pictland: Scotland to 795** by James Fraser (2009). ISBN 0978 07486 1232 1.
Vol. 2 **From Pictland to Alba (789-1070)** by Alex Woolf (2007). ISBN 978 07486 1234 5

When Duncan published in 1975 *Scotland: the Making of the Kingdom* as Volume1 of the Edinburgh History of Scotland it was hailed as a landmark in the writing of Scottish history, and the passage of a quarter of a century has not altered that verdict. That volume covered the period up to about 1286. In the interval a very great amount of work has been done that has transformed our knowledge of that difficult early period. A beginning was made by Professor Smyth, 1984, with *Warlords and Holy Men: Scotland AD 80-1000*. Now we have two volumes of the New Edinburgh History of Scotland, written by two of the experts who are doing so much to increase our understanding of that time.

These are the first volumes of the proposed ten volume History of Scotland, which promises to be as great a success as the earlier Edinburgh History. Volume 1 deals with the period between the departure of the Romans and the arrival of the Vikings. The end of Roman hegemony left Britain with regional groups competing for power. In Northumbria Anglo-Saxon mercenaries brought in by the Romans soon controlled Bernicia and Deira. The Votadini tribe known to us from Ptolomy's map occupied the Lothian area, and the name changed to the Goddodin. Their language was apparently a British p-Celtic language akin to Old Welsh, and later they, or at least part of their ruling class, moved to North Wales. To the west other British tribes controlled Cumbria and Strathclyde, forming the shadowy kingdom of Rheged and the better known Alt Clyd, based on Dumbarton Rock, the 'Fort of the Britons.' Kintyre and Argyll were occupied by speakers of a q-Celtic Irish Gaelic linked with their tribal relations in Ireland. Around the head of the Forth estuary were the Miathi, with the Manau area containing Clackmannan and Slammanan. To the North were the Picts. Their language was a form of p-Celtic.

The early history of North Britain, that was to become Scotland, is very difficult to discover because of the lack of documentation from the locality. We have to rely on records from elsewhere, especially from annals maintained in the Irish monasteries, such as the *Annals of Ulster, Annals of Tigernach*, etc. These were often in Old Irish, not Latin, whose exact translation may be unsure. Moreover we have no originals, only copies of copies, so there are likely to be scribal errors. Some information comes from the *Anglo-Saxon Chronicle*, and some from Bede's *Ecclesiastical History*, two more languages if it is necessary to work with the earliest copies! Works usually dismissed as mythology can also yield valuable clues if treated with due caution, for example Gildas' *The Ruin of Britain*, and many lives of the Saints, when disentangled from their standard hagiographical miracles. The *Prophecy of Berchán* has been shown to be history masquerading as prophecy, and although written in cryptic language can be useful. This list is by no means exhaustive. Clearly there is plenty of scope for anyone looking for puzzles to solve!

Historians are nowadays able and ready to supplement documentary evidence with the evidence from archaeology, so for example Fraser notes that recent archaeological work has shown that the Roman occupation lasted longer than we have usually believed, and that Tacitus gave credit to Agricola for what may have been the efforts of others. We have relied on the *Agricola* without allowing for it being a eulogy for Tacitus' father-in-law. Fraser says 'Certainly *Agricola* is open to the full range of critical analysis that has so revolutionised our understanding of such Early Historic writers as Bede and Adomnán'.

Fraser emphasises that although North Britain was only partly and for a relatively short time part of the Empire, Roman influence extended beyond its frontiers, and lasted after the withdrawal of its army. Things were never the same again, it was not a matter of a short Roman interlude then a return to the Iron Age, though of course many aspects of the lives of ordinary people hardly changed. Not least among the forces perpetuating the influence of Rome was the spread of Christianity. Fraser explains how this was carried out by such men as Ninian (Nyniau, Uinniau – names written in the different languages are often difficult to recognise as referring to the same individual), usually by persuading the king of the locality of the advantages of this strong new religion. There were of course then many 'kings', often no more than powerful war lords. Like Columba, Ninian had connections with the monasteries of Ireland, and monasteries began to be established in North Britain.

Pictish studies have made progress in many other ways in recent years. For example, matrilineal succession has been shown to be unnecessary to explain peculiarities in the King lists, and has been abandoned by modern scholars. (These lists, known as the *Chronical of the Kings of Alba* come to us in a medieval manuscript as a copy of much earlier documents. They are dealt with in detail by Marjorie Anderson in *Kings and Kingship in Early Scotland*). The Pictish region of Fortriu was taken by Skene in 1867 to be Strathearn, and has been accepted so long that its identity has become a 'factoid', i.e. a myth or hypothesis unchallenged for so long that it becomes accepted as a 'fact'. Only in 2006 was this challenged by Woolf; both he in Vol. II of this series and Fraser in Vol. I have shown that its position in Forres and Inverness as the Pictish zone north of the Mounth makes sense of much history of the periods in question.

Fraser is not content with the undoubted progress that has been made, and presents many questions that still remain to be answered. Nor is he always happy with accepted solutions, for example he is severely critical of the identification of Bede's *Giudi* with Stirling which has been accepted, among others, by the Ordnance Survey map of Dark Age Britain. He suggests that Cramond deserves consideration, but gives other possibilities.

It is impossible to list here in the space available all the topics dealt with in this volume of 436 pages. There are 25 genealogical tables with nearly 300 names, with little overlap. A Time Line from 69 A D to 795 is extremely useful, and there is an extensive Bibliography and Guide to Further Reading.

Woolf's Volume 2, (789-1070), in 384 pages deals with developments after the arrival of the Vikings. They came to the south coast of England in 789, and raided Lindisfarne in 793. Raids in the Hebrides brought them to Iona in 802. Monasteries were tempting targets likely to posses valuable (and portable) objects, perhaps vessels of gold or silver. They also housed the only people able to leave written records. These emphasised the sudden raid, the destruction and looting, and hence may have given a one-sided picture of the more complex activities of the vikings. The invaders soon began to stay on, demanding tribute. In c. 871 Olaf (Amlaíb) was killed when trying to collect tribute. They captured slaves and sold or exchanged these and their loot in emporia which they set up around the coasts of Europe, for example in Dublin and York, thus making a hugely important development of trade. No trading post has as yet been identified in Scotland, though Woolf discusses the possibility that Dumbarton could have been a *longphort* like Dublin.

The arrival of the Vikings did not stop the struggle for supremacy between the forces – war-bands, chiefdoms, petty kingdoms, etc., but it added a complicating factor. It may have had a decisive influence, for example, on the success of Kenneth Mac Alpin (Ciniod mac Elphin) in becoming King of the Picts.

These involved struggles are dealt with in detail in this volume. Woolf manages to disentangle the threads of the narrative with some skill, but to show the development of the kingdom of Scotland is not easy, and the reader must not expect an easy read.

Similar struggles for control were going on in southern Britain. The power of Wessex and Mercia were combined, so that by the first part of the tenth century Athelstan felt able to style himself 'King of all Britain'. In 925 he expelled Gothfrith the Viking king of York and gained Northumbria. In 927 at Eamont Bridge Constantine son of Áed, King of Scots and other kings of North Britain met Athelstan and acknowledged him as overlord. Perhaps to drive home the point, Athelstan invaded Scotland in 934 and having reached Dunottar withdrew apparently without meeting much opposition. Constantine reacted by forming an alliance with Sictric, son of Gothfrith, and a combined force of Irish Northmen and Scots met Athelstan at the battle of *Brunanburh,* the site of which has not yet been discovered. This was one of the great decisive battles of British history, effectively deciding the extent of English territory. Although Constantine was defeated, and one of his sons killed, he escaped, and reigned for 40 years, retiring to the monastery of St Andrews. Few kings survived in those times to retire. Constantine was a great Scottish king, deserving greater recognition.

Other north British kingdoms failed to survive. Woolf recounts what is known of, for example, Rheged and Strathclyde, and tells of the Battle of Carham (1018) gaining Lothian for Scotland and so establishing the main outlines of the kingdom.

Great progress towards understanding the history of this period has been made in recent years, although many puzzles remain. The contributions of ideas and discoveries of a number of other historians are acknowledged by both authors. These volumes throw much light on the history of early Scotland. It is no longer possible to talk of 'Dark Age Scotland', we must now call it 'Early Historic Scotland'.

No one interested in the period can afford to neglect these volumes.

Ron Page

INSTRUCTIONS TO AUTHORS

Title
Titles should be short. Authors' names should appear below the titles.

Contents
Any article relevant to the history, natural history or archaeology of the Forth Valley will be considered for publication. Articles describing the lives of locally important people or events are particularly welcome.

Articles should normally not exceed 8000 words; longer articles could be accepted if there is available space.

Text
Manuscripts should be submitted as Word documents on disc with an accompanying hard copy. High resolution figures and illustrations should be attached as separate TIFF or JPEG files.

Citations in the text are by name, followed by year e.g. Jones (1978); (Marwick, 1967; 1972).

Sources such as newspapers, books, etc. should be italicized e.g. *(Stirling Journal* 26 April 1890).

Archive citations should be written (Scottish Record Office AD58/48/74).

For historical papers sources may be noted in the text by a number and listed in the references.

Footnotes are not desirable.

Words of Latin origin e.g. *in situ* and Latin names of species should be italicized.

Common names of organisms should be in lower case throughout.

As far as practical metric measurements should be adopted using international standards.

Numbers should be used for all measurements e.g. 6 mm; 40 mm; 1000 ha.

In other use numbers ten and below should be spelt out, those above should not be e.g. six scientists, 40 flowers.

Abbreviations should be standardized: i.e. e.g., pers. comm., viz. etc. and not italicized.

Acronyms should be spelt out in full at the first mention and written without punctuation thereafter e.g. RSPB.

Notes and acknowledgements should precede the references, appendices should follow.

Figures and Tables
Illustrations and Tables should be submitted on separate sheets.

Illustrations should be of good contrast and the originals made available if required.

The dimensions of the printed page should be borne in mind viz.: – 172 x 110.5 mm excluding the running head.

Captions for Tables should appear above the Table, legends for Figures below.

Abbreviations should not be used to denote Table or Figure numbers e.g. Figure 1 not Fig 1.

References

These should be listed alphabetically in chronological order except that authorship with others should follow all sole publications by the same author irrespective of the year of publication.

Authors' names are not capitalized.

Titles of Journals should be in full, italicized and not abbreviated.

Volume number and inclusive pagination must be given.

Book titles should be italicized and the reference should give page numbers, place of publication and publisher in this order.

Titles of technical reports should not be italicized.

Examples of references

Thompson, D.B.A. and Hudson, P.J. 1992. Uplands moors and heaths. In *Managing Habitats for Conservation* (ed. W.J. Smith and D.A. Jones) pp. 290-310, Cambridge: Cambridge University Press.

Burnett, J.H. 1964. *The Vegetation of Scotland*. Edinburgh: Oliver and Boyd.

Evans, J. 1990. Managing to diversify forests. *Arboricultural Journal* 14, 373-378.

1 *Stirling Saturday Observer* 22, April 1882 p3.

2 *The Chronicle of Walter Guisborough,* ed. H. Rothwell. Cambden Society London 1957 pp299, 295-6.

3 National Archives of Scotland. CC21/5 Stirling Commissionary Court, register of testaments.